FLIGHT TESTING at EDWARDS

Flight Test Engineers' Stories
1946–1975

FLIGHT TESTING *at* EDWARDS

Flight Test Engineers' Stories
1946–1975

Edited by Fred Stoliker, Bob Hoey, and Johnny Armstrong

Flight Test Historical Foundation

ISBN 0-9713702-0-6

Printed in USA

Cover by Doug Nelson
Published by the Flight Test Historical Foundation
44916 N. 10th Street West
Lancaster, CA 93534
(661) 723-1574

Second printing, 2001, in cooperation with
Walsworth Publishing Company
306 North Kansas Avenue
Marceline, Missouri 64658

TABLE OF CONTENTS

FOREWORD

I was very pleased when I learned that the Flight Test Engineers of Edwards were putting together a book about Flight Testing. They should know better than anyone what happened during the flight tests that were conducted between 1946 and 1975. I had the privilege of knowing most of these flight test engineers while much of the flight testing was going on. Some flew with me, others I met with on a regular basis and some I knew from observation or from meetings or social gatherings. They were a relatively small group who had a large impact on the successful testing of many aircraft. The term "aircraft" is meant to include fixed wing, rotary wing, gliders, and all means of propulsion. They were the test engineers for anything that flew at Edwards.

Today, test programs are conducted using large test forces, sophisticated computer systems, intensive safety reviews and many levels of management and supervision. Especially during the early part of the time period that this book covers, the flight tests were done by what I would describe as a flight test team. That team usually consisted of a pilot, a flight test engineer, an instrumentation technician and the aircraft crew chief. They each had supervisors or commanders who could give directions, but most of the time the team was allowed to do the job with only a small amount of guidance.

The pilot or the flight test engineer usually acted as the team leader. However a team leader was seldom designated. The pilot or flight test engineer with the strongest personality or the most experience became the de facto leader. Hazardous test approvals were received after explaining to the Chief of Test Operations or the Flight Test Engineering Supervisor what was planned. If the pilot and the flight test engineer considered the test to be nonhazardous they would go ahead, on their own.

On many of these flight tests, the flight test engineer went on the flight. Most of them felt that they got better data when they were on board. Some had queasy stomachs, but they went anyway. During the latter part of the period the flight test teams began to receive more supervision and computers came into more common use. The team quickly learned how to pacify management and still get the job done in an efficient manner. The computers made some things easier, but the long slide rules were still in use and frequently used to check on the computer accuracy.

Almost all of the pilots were graduates of a Test Pilot School but there was no school for flight test engineers at that time. They came to Edwards as young college graduates in the engineering disciplines; aeronautical, mechanical, electrical, etc. The road to becoming a flight test engineer was study and on-the-job training. There were several senior test engineers who were good teachers and role models. Paul Bikle and Jack Strier are two that come to mind. These and many others helped to train and inspire the young flight test engineers.

The flight test engineers at Edwards generally worked in relative obscurity and without much recognition. They planned the test program, coordinated the mission with flight operations and with aircraft maintenance, and then flew on many of the missions gathering the data. The hard part then came. It required many hours to interpret and plot the data. The final steps were to put the data into the report and then integrate pilot and flight test engineer's comments into a final report. Sometimes the test results weren't what management or the Project Office at Wright-Patterson wanted or expected. At times the results showed adverse characteristics for the aircraft and the manufacturer would be upset. The flight test engineers that I know always stood their ground and if the data showed adverse characteristics, that was the way the report went out.

The work of the flight test engineers has led to better aircraft or flight vehicles for the military, the airlines, general aviation and the space program. Some of them, along with pilots and other crew members, lost their lives while performing this important duty.

During my flight testing years I was privileged to work with the editors of this book. They made important contributions during their time as flight test engineers and I think that they are making another important contribution by gathering and preserving these stories. Future generations will be provided with real lessons and will be able to recall the excitement, humor, and sometimes the tragedy, that went along with flight testing at Edwards in the early years.

Fitz Fulton

Fitzhugh L. (Fitz) Fulton Jr.

PREFACE

We have been asked many times why we would want to undertake the task of contacting people, gathering stories, and having a book of flight test engineering stories published.

To us, the answer was straightforward and simple! Every time a group of flight test engineers get together they start swapping stories about the programs that they or one of their friends has conducted or participated in. The stories may be humorous, or how we got scared, or how someone dreamed up a new way to conduct a flight test, or how we enjoyed the adrenaline rush of participating in the flight test of the most modern military systems, or ....

Unfortunately, as time passes we find that there are fewer and fewer people around who remember or participated in these stories and we wanted to preserve the events, thoughts, and emotions of these "unknowns", those who planned test programs, rode along as technical observers during tests, gathered, reduced, and analyzed test data, and, with the test pilots, wrote the test reports. We're proud of the role that we played in evaluating the aircraft that became part of the US Air Force and Army capability; providing the data that led to decisions to include or not include a specific aircraft or concept in the operational inventory; and provide the data for the Flight Manual — the operational bible for the users of the aircraft. Not to be forgotten is the research aircraft development and test capability that evolved at the present day NASA-Dryden Flight Research Center as well as the Air Force Flight Test Center.

We were pleased at the number of people who responded to our "call" for stories and at the same time disappointed about the stories that we didn't get. We are deeply grateful to those who took the time to write down their recollections—and it has been a joy to get stories from people that we had not heard from for 30 years or more. However, there are many more stories that remain to be told.

All of us flight test engineers owe a debt of gratitude to the test pilots who flew the varied test aircraft. Many of the names mentioned have received world-wide acclaim, others did not receive this deserved accolade. We entrusted our lives with these people and they obviously brought us through some "mighty" adventures — we and they are still around to tell our stories. They mentored us when we were fresh out of college and hopefully, we were able to provide some mentoring to those fresh out of the Test Pilot School as we gained experience. (We do not wish to imply that FTEs are exposed to the same level of risk as the test pilots. Most of the high performance aircraft and all of the research aircraft are single seaters. Also, tests that are considered "hazardous" are usually flown with a minimum crew which may or may not inclue an FTE.)

From the perspective of history, many of the events reported appear not to have been well thought out. However, it must be noted that flight test techniques and safety of flight considerations were continually evolving and continue to do so. The aircraft, by present day standards, were relatively unsophisticated as were data acquisition and processing techniques. For example, in the early days of jets there was an urgency to get every last bit of data possible when you were airborne and the engines were working properly. The engine time between overhauls was often 5 to 10 hours, and when they worked you kept going. In addition, there was a tendency to underestimate their voracious appetite for fuel as compared to the "recips." So what if you ran low on fuel. The wings were large, the gliding speeds were slow, and a deadstick landing on the lakebed was no big deal. After all, that's why you were at Edwards, for that great big runway sometimes called a lake bed.

As we, the flight test team, learned how to avoid the mistakes of the past, these understandings became "codified" in the regulations and operating procedures that now govern flight testing. Certainly all the rules, regulations and review boards take great amounts of time and immense amounts of energy and, no doubt frustrate our present day brethren; however, very few pilots or engineers have lost their lives in recent years. We are sure that some had "scares", "fun", or terrorized some segment of the civilian populace, etc., but they are here. We hope that they will continue to improve the capability to conduct tests safely, and tell their stories to future generations.

We thank the Air Force, Army, and NASA for giving us the opportunity to participate in this great adventure!

The Editors would like to thank each of the authors for taking the time to record their experiences and memories. We would like to acknowledge the help, advice, encouragement, and support provided by the Air Force Flight Test Center History Office during each step of this project, with a special thanks to Fred Johnsen of that office, and to Nathan R. "Rosie" Rosengarten, Col. USAF Ret., Founder and President, Wright Patterson AFB Educational Fund and Member, Wright Stuff Association. We want to thank Doug Nelson, Director of the AFFTC Museum, for creating the striking cover. We owe a debt of gratitude to Attorney Thomas J. Ward for his legal advice. A special note of thanks must be extended to the Board of the Edwards Flight Test Historical Foundation who provided the financial support to ensure that this collection of stories would be published.

Fred Stoliker, Bob Hoey, and Johnny Armstrong

DEDICATION

Flight testing is a wonderful occupation. Where else can you constantly be on the cutting edge of aerospace technology?

Flight testing is also a "team sport" — a team that is built around the test pilot and the test engineer. And, as in any team operation, there has to be mutual confidence and trust between these team members because flight testing can be hazardous to your health. The importance of this team work and the need for mutual confidence was dramatically clear to me as Jackie Ridley and I conducted the tests of the X-1 that lead to the breaching of the "sonic wall." I ventured into this unknown region of flight with complete trust and confidence in Jackie's aeronautical knowledge and, more importantly, his skepticism of some of the theories. I was always aware of his concern for my safety and his cautious, yet practical approach to each flight.

After our X-1 work Jackie, along with Paul Bikle, became the key figures in building the flight test engineering capability that exists at Edwards AFB. They nurtured a fledgling flight test engineering organization and built a world-renowned capability that grew in parallel with the test pilot capabilities fostered by the USAF Test Pilot School and the Flight Test Operations. If the test aircraft has more than one seat, the flight test engineer will ride with the pilot during flight to operate instrumentation, record data, and adjust the test flight as necessary to match the airborne capabilities of the aircraft and the data recording systems. If something doesn't work according to plan, the engineer and the pilot will figure out what can be done to effectively utilize the available flight time.

As I noted above, flight testing can be hazardous. Sometimes there are accidents where flight crews are lost — including flight test engineers. The following is the listing that we could confirm at the time of publication, from Air Force Flight Test Center records, US Army Aviation Engineering

Flight Activity, and contacts with people in the aircraft industry, of Flight Test Engineers who lost their lives while performing official duties at Edwards. To them we dedicate this book!

Chuck Yeager

Charles E. Yeager, Brig. General, USAF (Retired)

FLIGHT TEST ENGINEER FATALITY LIST
EDWARDS AFB

Year	Aircraft	Engineer(s)	Affiliation	Pilot(s)
1948	XB-49	Claire C. Lesser	USAF	Capt. Glen Edwards
		Charles H. LaFountain	USAF	Maj. Daniel Forbes
1951	B-50D	Charles White	Ryan	Maj. Gordon Payne
		Wallace Christian	Ryan	Capt. William Bailey
1953	YF-89D	Jack M. Collingworth	Northrop	Walter P. Jones
1955	B-57B	Nobuo R. "Bob" Sunada	USAF	Capt. Anderson Hontz
1955	A3D	Willard J. Amick	Douglas	William Davis
1958	A3D	Dale A. Benethum	Douglas	Thomas G. Kilgariff
1964	LOH-5	Robert Turk	USA	
1970	Guppy 101	Warren "Sam" Walker	Convair	Van Shepard
1971	C-5A	Capt. Ronald Frank	USAF	(Ground Accident)
1972	YF-4D	Lt.Col.Joseph P. Waters	USAF	Capt. John D. Evans
1974	OV-1D	Capt. Kenneth Schranz	USA	Maj. Frederick Daniloff
1976	Bell 214	Emmett Laing	USA	Capt. Gary Hill
1982	OV-1D	John "Dave" Ottomeyer	USA	CW3 Hugh Lammons
1986	F-4C	Maj. Ronald J. Faris	USAF	
1992	C-23A	William Abbott	USA	Robert Robins

INTRODUCTION

Near the end of World War Two (WWII) the Army Air Forces (USAAF) (soon to become the U.S. Air Force) needed a better location than Wright Field near Dayton, Ohio, for conducting flight tests. The increasing test load, the introduction of jet engines, the requirement for improved safety, and the need for security, resulted in a decision to establish a permanent flight test base at a spot in the southern California desert that was perfect for testing airplanes. It had great flying weather, was in a remote area with sparse population, and, best of all, had a 5 by 10-mile, hard-surface, dry lake bed that could be used for takeoffs and landings by the heaviest of airplanes.

Muroc Army Air Field was utilized during WWII to perform some classified and hazardous flight tests including early tests of the Bell XP-59, the first US jet-powered aircraft. Shortly after the end of WWII, the National Advisory Committee for Aeronautics (NACA) sent Walt Williams with a small contingent of NACA pioneers to Muroc where they teamed with a few USAAF and Bell test folks to test the rocket-powered X-1 research airplane. From these simple beginnings, Edwards Air Force Base evolved; a 305,000-acre premier facility with all of the necessary capabilities for the flight testing of prototype, production, and research aircraft. It is currently home to the Air Force Flight Test Center, the National Aeronautics and Space Administration (NASA) Dryden Flight Research Center, the Army Aviation Engineering Flight Activity, and various aircraft contractor test teams.

The following stories occurred during this growth period at Edwards. They are presented in roughly chronological order. Key events describing the growth of Edwards AFB, as well as other world events, are interspersed between the stories to help the reader place the stories historically. This chronological sequence also helps to highlight the variety of aircraft in test at any one time, and the concurrency of many of the activities.

Each of the authors was a flight test engineer (FTE) participating in some type of testing at Edwards. Some were military FTE's serving a normal 2- to 5-year tour of duty at Edwards. A few were also rated military pilots who had completed the AF Test Pilot School, but were serving in FTE assignments. These rated officers often assumed both piloting and engineering duties on some of the smaller test programs. Many of the authors were Air Force, Army, or NACA/NASA career civil service employees. Each author writes to a different audience. Some are writing to their buddies at the bar; some to young FTE's; and some to historians or others in the technical community. The stories have received only limited editing for clarity in the hopes that the personalities of the individual authors will be retained. The occurrence of most of the events (but not the details) are verifiable by the compiling editors. The details are from the memories of the individual authors and may suffer from the effect of the ensuing 20 to 50 years.

The stories begin in 1946 when the AAF was just beginning to test jet-powered bombers at Muroc Army Air Field. Here are the flight test engineers' stories of the early days at Edwards.

"DATA ON ..."

A FIRST JET RIDE - XB-46
by Richard A. Schmidt

It was during the summer of 1946 that I had my first flight in a jet airplane. Captain Glen Edwards was the pilot for the flight tests of the four-jet Convair XB-46 aircraft and Paul Bikle was the test engineer while Claire Lesser was the assistant test engineer. Paul gave me the opportunity to replace Claire on one flight. All takeoffs and landings were done on the dry lakebed where there were no markings or lights that one could use to judge speed. The airplane had a large plexiglass cone-shaped nose next to where I sat to record data. From that position I had a good view of the lakebed in front of us.

I could hear that Glen had increased the engine RPM, and therefore the thrust, and we began our takeoff roll. It was so quiet forward of the engines that I didn't think that he had applied takeoff power. I knew that we had at least four miles of lakebed in front of us but surely he wasn't going to takeoff without the use of full power! I never did hear any increase in power but I could see that we were moving. Since the airspeed indicator doesn't move until you reach 50 mph I had no idea how fast we were going or how fast we were accelerating because of the lack of visual cues. It was a strange sensation! Finally the needle came off the peg and our speed was increasing quite rapidly. Obviously my instincts were wrong, he did have full power and we were about to lift off.

Convair XB-46 takeoff from Rogers dry lakebed.

Convair XB-46 with test crew: (Left to right) Capt. Glen Edwards, Capt. Bosworth, Paul Bikle, Claire Lesser.

Not only was the takeoff a new experience, but climb out and level flight were essentially noiseless. With a jet airplane's ability to cruise at 35,000 to 40,000 feet and therefore above most turbulent air, this was the only way to travel cross country. This jet airplane was so smooth and quiet that I thought, in 1947, that the airlines should order jets right away. I learned later that there was good reason for not ordering — these engines had to be overhauled after only 15 to 25 hours of operation. Today, a jet engine is overhauled at over 25,000 hours.

The flight was otherwise uneventful, including the landing on the wide expanse of Rogers Dry Lake.

§

With the end of the WWII came a recognition that military airpower was the wave of the future. The U.S. Army Air Forces became the U.S Air Force. The organization was elevated to the same status as the Army and the Navy, and Muroc Army Airfield became Muroc Air Force Base.

The Edwards landscape was not only being rocked by the new sound of jet engines, there was another thunder being heard—rocket engines! The X-1 had arrived! A tiny, bullet-like research airplane, it was being dropped from the belly of a B-29 and was beginning its assault on the sound barrier. Capt. Chuck Yeager made the historic first supersonic flight on Oct. 14, 1947.

Rocket-powered research airplanes of various shapes and designs would continue to fly at Edwards for the next 28 years.

F-84B PERFORMANCE TESTS
by Richard A. Schmidt

In the spring of 1947, I was assigned to write a test plan to determine the performance of six—right, six not one—Republic F-84Bs. It was decided to

Republic straight-wing F-84.

run performance tests on six airplanes because the data showed a considerable variation of performance from one airplane to another. The tests were to be flown at the then Muroc AAF. It was now June 1947 and as a relatively newly graduated engineer I was unable to buy a car — not even a good used car. So I was stuck on the Mojave desert without wheels and no public transportation to take us into Los Angeles, only about 100 miles away. And I was to be there for three months.

I was the only test engineer assigned to all six airplanes and I quickly learned that it was a lot easier to gather the data than to keep up with reducing it to Standard Day conditions.

The variation in speed of the F-84Bs in level flight was attributed to a variation in thrust of the jet engines when set at the same RPM. The engines were calibrated for thrust in a test cell before being installed in the airplane but we decided that their thrust had to be measured while installed in the airplane. No thrust stand was available anywhere in the U.S. that could accommodate a complete fighter airplane, so I had to design a fixture with which to measure the thrust. We had load cells about the size of softballs that were used to weigh an airplane but we had to make a horizontal measurement. I designed a fixture that would convert the "pull" of the airplane under power into a "push" on the weight cell. It was one of the few times that my classes in "Strength of Materials" and calculations of stress and strain were put to use.

We measured thrust variations as expected, but upon further investigation we found that the variations were actually occurring in the engine rpm gage! It was in Barney Oldfield's Instrumentation Laboratory at Muroc that they discovered that, as the gage warmed up in the first 15 to 20 minutes, the calibration changed. But that's what tests are all about, to find answers to otherwise unexplainable results.

FLIGHT TEST OF THE XB-45
by Richard A. "Dick" Schmidt

In 1947 I was assigned to conduct the performance and flying qualities tests of the North American Aviation XB-45 which was in competition with the XB-46.

The tests went along pretty smoothly except for a couple of interesting landings. On one flight we ran completely out of fuel just as we were beginning our approach. So here we were, out of gas and headed for a landing somewhere. I knew that we were within gliding distance of Rogers Dry Lake at Muroc with its miles of good landing area. I also knew that the pilot

North American XB-45 with test crew: (Left to right) Dick Schmidt, Maj. Bob Cardenas, Capt. Glen Edwards, Maj. Danny Forbes.

had been trained in gliders at one point in his career so I was not much concerned about this "dead stick" landing, but not so the co-pilot. My seat, as the test engineer, was down alongside the tandem seats of the pilot and co-pilot where I could see and record the instrument readings and operate the photo panel. As I looked up and back into the co-pilot's face I could see the beads of perspiration and noted that he was wiping his obviously sweaty palms on his knees. About this time I looked out the nose window to see that we were about to touch down on the edge of the dry lake where a barbed wire fence had been strung to keep cattle off the lake bed.

Just about the time that the wheels should have touched the ground, I felt the pilot pulling up on the controls so that we would clear the barbed wire fence. Sure enough we stalled and dropped onto the lakebed on the other side of the fence. No harm was done to the fence or the airplane. When we got out of the plane, I asked the pilot "Why didn't you just land before we got to the fence? Ripping out the fence would not have hurt the plane and the fence wouldn't take much to repair." His answer was "We were here at Muroc on TDY and the Muroc pilots resented our doing all the test flying for the Air Force. I could just see all the nasty letters going back and forth between Muroc and Wright Field about negligence on my part."

The other landing incident caused a little more damage. Again, we were trying to stretch our data gathering during the flight, and we were scheduled to make a performance landing at the end of the flight. In a performance landing, the aircraft is flown over an imaginary 50-foot high obstacle at minimum approach speed. The touchdown is made as soon as possible and full braking is applied until the aircraft comes to a full stop. The event was recorded photographically through a calibrated grid so that distances could be accurately measured.

Again we ran out of fuel — but this time we were already just off the end of the concrete runway. Because we no longer had any thrust in the engines, we descended more rapidly than normal. Looking out through the nose window, I could see that we were going to land short of the runway! We made a pretty hard landing and I figured that we would bounce and then hit again — but no second hit! I couldn't believe that we hadn't bounced after hitting that hard. On getting out of the airplane we discovered that the left gear was almost torn off the wing. A lot of rivets were popped in the wheel well and not much was holding the gear in place. The reason we hadn't bounced was that the wheels had made a crater about a foot deep in the hard desert adobe soil on impact and thereby cushioned the landing.

Our final report on the XB-45 showed no major deficiencies.

We flew back to Wright Field in a C-54. General Boyd was aboard the flight but got off at Scott AFB near St. Louis to attend a football game. A relatively junior test pilot took over as pilot and proceeded to perform a Chandelle on take-off! You know that he did not expect General Boyd to observe that violation of regulations. I would not have believed that someone would try such a stunt if I hadn't been aboard. I have to give him credit for pilot proficiency because it was a very elegant maneuver. But when General Boyd got back to Wright Field, he chewed the ass out of this test pilot If we had fallen through as we did when I was in a B-24 out of Lowry Field, we surely would have "bought the farm."

§

Flight testing of these new jets was not without its losses. NACA lost its first test pilot (Howard Lilly) in the crash of the Navy/Douglas D-558-I research airplane. Capt. Glen Edwards, Maj. Daniel Forbes, two civilian flight test engineers, and a military flight engineer were killed in the crash of the XB-49, a prototype flying wing bomber, and forerunner to today's B-2 stealth bomber.

Production jet fighters began to roll off the production line: the P-80 Shooting Star (the first product of the Lockheed "Skunk Works"), North American's XP-86 "Sabre", Republic's F-84 "Thunderjet". These airplanes were not far behind the X-1 in the quest for higher speed. In 1948, the XP-86 (later F-86) was the first production fighter to exceed Mach One in a shallow dive.

CO-PILOT ON B-45 FLIGHT TESTS
by Richard A. "Dick" Schmidt

I was assigned as the co-pilot for the performance tests of the B-45A in 1948 — the only civilian to be so assigned from the Flight Test Division.

As the test engineer for the XB-45, I sat on a tall wooden draftsman's stool in the access aisle alongside the tandem seats of the pilot and co-pilot. Flying as the co-pilot/engineer made it a lot easier to perform as the test engineer even though I was occasionally called upon to "take over" for the pilot.

On our first test flight we had arranged for an F-86 pacer aircraft to assist in the calibration of the airspeed system. By the time we reached 25,000 feet we had not heard from the pacer pilot. The pilot asked me to take over the controls and continue the climb to 35,000 feet while he tried several different radio channels in order to contact the pacer pilot. When we reached 35,000 feet I leveled off and the speed quickly increased because the power was still set for a performance climb. Very soon the force required to maintain level flight became very heavy—so heavy that I had to put my feet up to assist my arms—and I couldn't get the pilot's attention because he was trying various air-to-air radio channels. There was no trim switch on the co-pilot stick so I was unable to relieve the forces. Finally, the pilot came back on intercom and I got him to trim out the control forces. Needless to say, one of our first recommendations was to install a trim tab switch on the co-pilot's stick.

The pacer pilot was to meet us at 35,000 feet. He came over the radio saying he was at 35, 000 feet over Muroc but didn't see us. The B-45

North American B-45A with test crew. L to r: Capt. "Robby" Robinson, Dick Schmidt, (unidentified).

pilot, Captain "Robbie" Robinson, replied that we were over the west end of Antelope Valley, to which the pacer pilot responded "Good, I'll come meet you."

We were cruising at about 500 mph looking intently for the pacer when suddenly, a blurred object whizzed under us from front to rear. The pacer pilot came over the radio "The moment I caught sight of you, I was heading straight at you, head on. I dumped the stick as fast as I could to avoid you but I wasn't sure I was going to make it." He was also cruising at about 500 mph so our closing speed was 1000 mph — faster than a bullet. It was stark terror when we realized the literal "close call" we had just experienced.

The remaining seven flights were conducted without any particularly interesting incidents..

1948 BENDIX TROPHY RACE
by Richard A. "Dick" Schmidt

The Bendix Trophy Race which was held in conjunction with the National Air Races in Cleveland started at Long Beach, California and was timed by the National Aeronautics Association (NAA). In 1948, the Air Force did not have an airplane that qualified for entry under the criteria established under the chairmanship of the Navy. Needless to say, the Air Force was not very happy and hatched a plan to make the Navy rue their decision.

The Navy was planning to use four of their FJ-1 combat jets for the Race; however, the FJ-1 could not make it non-stop from Long Beach to Cleveland and would have to land and refuel enroute. The Air Force calculated that the T-33 equipped with the larger P-38 tip tanks should be able to make the trip non-stop. If so, the trainer aircraft should be able to reach Cleveland faster and would surely embarrass the Navy. The plan was to have the T-33 make the flight on the day before the race but to have the time certified by the National Aeronautics Association (NAA). Since the T-33 was just coming off the line and had not yet been turned over to the Air Force, the airplane to be used was "borrowed" from Lockheed.

The entire planning and negotiating with Lockheed was done out of Wright Field but since I was already in California, I was assigned to gather the flight data for this configuration. Captain "Fitz" Fitzgerald was to be the pilot for the effort.

On the appointed day, Fitz and I flew down to Lockheed in a T-6. We met with their chief designer, Kelly Johnson, and their test pilots Tony Levier and "Fish" Salmon. It was decided that since the maximum range could be obtained by cruising at the Service Ceiling, that Fitz and I should obtain speed power data at 45,000 feet to verify fuel flow rate at that altitude. The P-38 tanks were considerably larger than the P-80 tip tanks for which the speed power and fuel flow data were at hand.

The runway at Van Nuys was not as long as one would wish for a jet take-off or even a landing, especially if you were fully loaded with fuel as we were. We got off OK and were climbing north at a pretty good rate until we got to about 40,000 feet. By then our rate of climb was down to about 50 feet per minute. At that rate it would take forever to reach our goal of 45,000 feet. Fitz continued to fly north with the full intention of getting into a standing wave over Bishop, California.

Once in the wave we immediately started to climb at about 150 ft per min until we reached 45,000 feet. We got the speed power and fuel flow data and flew back to Van Nuys. We were soon on our downwind leg and turning for final approach. High power electric lines were located just off the approach end of the runway and Fitz was sweating it out. He wanted to be flying as slow as safely possible over the high power lines so that we could drop unto the runway quickly and at a slow enough speed to stop rolling by the end of the runway. As we taxied up to the Lockheed hangar, he wiped the sweat off his brow.

The test data proved our calculations accurate so we returned to Muroc AFB for a few days to await the day before the Bendix Trophy Race when the Navy jets were to make their speed run. On that day before, we went to Long Beach where Lockheed had already flown the T-33 with the oversize P-38 tanks. We had an official timer from NAA on hand but the airport was "socked in." The ceiling and visibility readings were below minimums. It was early in the morning but to fly non-stop to Cleveland that day required an early morning take-off. A few strings were pulled and the minimums were declared acceptable long enough for Fitz to get off the ground. The official timer said "What time is it?", got his answer, and waved Fitz on the runway. To this day, I don't know if the timer was serious in asking the time of day.

After Fitz flew off into the fog, I returned to Muroc AFB to continue my F-84 test program but kept in touch with word of his progress. Fitz was reported passing over Pueblo, Colo. and doing O.K. A short time later he reported having a problem switching the fuel flow from a different tank and was returning to Pueblo to land. He had to abort the race. Upon a thorough examination of the airplane's fuel system it was concluded that it was only a faulty indication. He was on or ahead of his flight schedule and could have made Cleveland in less time than the Navy did the following day. Nonetheless, it made the Air Force feel good about their new jet trainer, and it had provided me an opportunity to fly in the standing wave at 45,000 feet in a jet!

§

The quest for higher speed continued as did the search for more knowledge on performance and handling qualities in the transonic and supersonic flight regime. NACA established the High Speed Flight Station at Edwards to continue the research work on rocket-powered and other X-category research airplanes. Yeager continued to fly the X-1 along with several NACA pilots. He was soon joined by two more Air Force pilots, Capts. Bob Hoover and "Pete" Everest. Major Jack Ridley was the key Air Force flight test engineer supporting the X-1 program since the beginning of the program along with the NACA engineers. He eventually became the Chief of the Engineering Division at the Air Force Flight Test Center. (Jack was killed during a routine flight in a C-47 "Gooney Bird" in Japan shortly after his reassignment from Edwards in 1955.)

WHEN ENGINEERS FLY ROCKETSHIPS
by Frank K. "Pete" Everest

Major Jack Ridley was the test engineer on the X-1 project with Yeager and I. Jack was a brilliant engineer. He was the first man to devise a formula on how to measure thrust at various altitudes. But the story is that, due to Jack's efforts, Yeager and I decided he ought to be checked out in the X-1. Albeit, Jack was NOT an outstanding pilot, he was a good one. He did not have any combat, or a large amount of flying time — his love was engineering, whereas Yeager and I loved to fly.

Having monitored ALL the X-1 flights, Jack was familiar with the approach speeds and he knew the inner workings of the X-1 as well as anyone. So Yeager and I took off as chase pilots for Jack's flight. Climb to altitude was as scheduled. Jack pressurized the fuel systems, countdown to drop started and he was dropped on schedule. After drop he started the rocket engines and started his climb to altitude and subsequent speed run. Shortly after drop, Jack called out "I smell smoke — I must be on fire!" Yeager and I could see the outside of the X-1 and everything was normal so we figured he had some electrical short, but, as the X-1 cockpit was pressurized with nitrogen, there was absolutely no danger of fire. So Yeager replied that there was no fire and that there was nothing in the cockpit that could burn. After a few seconds Jack replied in his Oklahoma twang, "Like hell there isn't — I'm in here!!"

FLIGHT TESTS OF THE XF-92
by Richard A. "Dick" Schmidt

The XF-92 was built as a prototype by Convair to evaluate the handling qualities of a "Delta Wing"— a "tailless" design. (This configuration was later used in the F-102, F-106, and B-58 aircraft.)

In 1949, Chuck Yeager and I went to Muroc to conduct the Air Force's first flight tests of the XF-92. Since we were testing a prototype, we were not particularly concerned about the overall performance of the airplane but de-

Convair XF-92A with Capt. Chuck Yeager in the cockpit.

signed the tests primarily to evaluate the delta wing and tail flying character-istics as well as stability and control features.

Chuck was particularly impressed with the rate of roll available. The large vertical tail contributed to the aileron effectiveness in a roll when the rudder was also displaced in a direction that supplemented the roll force of the ailerons. The extremely high rate of roll would be very useful in a "dog fight." That high roll rate caused Chuck to exclaim: "When I'm doing a maximum rate of roll, it feels like the seat of my pants are pushed down into the seat while at the same time the centrifugal force is pulling my head up toward the canopy."

Chuck included in our test report: "This would make one heck of a fighter plane."

While the Air Force did not proceed with a delta wing airplane de-sign at that time, the British were interested in utilizing the delta wing design configuration on a bomber they were designing. I was called to a meeting at Wright Field with some British designers who wanted to know if we found any drawbacks in the performance and stability and control of the delta wing. I gave them encouragement. A few years later they were flying their delta wing bomber which I believe they called the Vulcan.

§

The advantages of the remote location, good weather and security at Muroc were evident to the AF Managers at Wright Field. They established a permanent contingent of flight test personnel on site in 1950 at about the time of the start of the Korean war. Many of the Air Force test activities were being conducted at Edwards but were still managed out of Wright Field, while others were being conducted at contractor facilities but managed out of Edwards. In January of 1950 the name of the base was officially changed from "Muroc" to "Edwards" in memory of Capt. Glen Edwards who died in the crash of the XB-49.

B-36D TESTS
by Billy F. Owens

In the fall of 1950 I was assigned to go from Wright Field where I was stationed to Carswell AFB, Texas, to support the B-36D performance tests. Preflight preparations were very extensive to get "six turning", then about 45 minutes for checkout of the very extensive instrumentation system, and then

Convair B-36D "Peacemaker."

taxi to the runway and get "four burning", set the take-off power on all 10 engines before starting the take-off roll. Many of the flights were of six- to ten-hour duration.

One morning we were testing the B-36 climb rate and maximum altitude at very light weight — about 210,000 to 240,000 pounds, as I recall. Right after take-off and wheels up, a Vought F4U Corsair (WWII gull wing, Marine Corps fighter) from nearby Vought Aircraft joined us and proceeded to show us his rate of climb. After a few minutes, we rapidly climbed away from him and left him far below. He had no way of knowing we were such light weight.

I often wondered how he explained to himself how that big bomber out-climbed his fighter aircraft.

C-124A PHASE IV PERFORMANCE AND FLYING QUALITIES
by Fred Stoliker

In the fall of 1950, I was assigned as part of the test team to conduct Phase IV Performance and Flying Qualities on the C-124A Globemaster II aircraft. The crew consisted of pilot Captain Tom Cecil, co-pilot Lt. Bob Hippert, flight engineers Captain Don Mimeau and M/Sgt. Jack Sowers, head flight test engineer (FTE) Bill Magruder (GS-7), and assistant FTE me. (GS-5). We departed Wright Field and gathered at the Douglas Plant in Long Beach from which we conducted all of the early tests.

The C-124A was a HUGE airplane — at least to a relatively new flight test engineer like me — and I certainly felt that it lived up to its nickname of "The Great Aluminum Cloud." It was also called the "Douglas Vibrator" because of the high vibration experienced throughout the aircraft, especially at normal rated power. It was a low-wing monoplane and had four R4360 Pratt and Whitney 28-cylinder "corncob" engines. There were clamshell doors in the nose that covered integral ramps which were utilized for the roll-on, roll-off loading of cargo to the main deck. There were a series of small cargo bays reached by trap doors in the main floor where small, low density loads could be carried. There was also an "upper deck" that could be lowered into place about six feet above the main floor to carry cargo. In addition, provisions were provided to carry passengers/paratroopers in bucket seats along the sides of the fuselage. The maximum operating weight was 210,000 ponds with 175,000 pounds being the normal operating weight. All-in-all, a large, usable aircraft — but the thing that impressed me the most was the landing gear. It looked as if it had been designed by civil engineers accustomed to building bridges and the main gear tires were four feet in diameter!

Zero g flight in a C-124A

As was normal at that time, there was an airspeed "trailing bomb" to measure static pressure to assist in calibrating the airspeed system. The bomb and its capstan — which was operated by a human powered crank — were installed in the aircraft's tail cone behind the aft bulkhead. The procedure was for me as the junior (and dumbest) member of the crew to leave the

Douglas C-124A "Globemaster."

cockpit, walk to the aft bulkhead, take off my parachute, and climb through the bulkhead door, hand-feed the bomb through a door about 14 inches long and 6 inches wide at one end and about 4 inches at the other, and then crank out the bomb to its proper position. Then I would retrace my steps get back to my navigator's station where the photopanel was installed so that I could hand-record data and operate the camera switch.

One day when we were conducting stall tests, the airspeed system began to fluctuate widely when we neared the stall buffet boundary. After a short discussion, it was decided that I would go back to the tail cone and look through the door to observe what was happening to the bomb. Dutifully I went back to the bulkhead, took off my parachute and crawled into the tailcone trailing an intercom wire. When I reported in position, Captain Cecil performed a series of power off stall approaches with various combinations of flaps and gear and I carefully reported what the bomb was doing — and took notes as best I could. Then a power on stall approach with take-off flaps and gear down was initiated. I should note here that the power off stalls in all configurations were quite mild and the nose fell through very nicely. As flap settings were increased the bomb started performing greater and greater gyrations. However, all those mild characteristics disappeared when power on stalls were attempted — there was a sharp nose down pitch accompanied by a pronounced roll-off. What that meant to me was that I became free floating in the tail cone and I grabbed at anything that came near in order to stabilize myself. Naturally some of the handiest things around were the control cables and Captain Cecil was not all that happy that I was hanging from them while he was trying to recover from a stall.

From that point on we did not utilize an observer in the tail cone.

A bouncing lead ball

The test crew departed Wright Field and gathered at the Douglas Plant in Long Beach from which we conducted all of the early tests. In those days the airport was fairly isolated except that a popular waterhole "The Bomb Shelter" was located on Lakewood Blvd. — almost squarely on the approach end of the main runway.

The aircraft was powered by four Pratt & Whitney (P&W) designed engines that were produced by the Ford Motor Company at a Chicago, Illinois plant. Other than being built by Ford, the biggest difference between our engines and those being used in other aircraft such as the B-36 was that our engines had a two-speed turbo-compressor that featured an automatic phase-in between low and high blower speeds that was supposed to provide full power to higher altitudes. For reasons I never understood, the engines were not providing the expected power in the region between full low blower and full high blower so P&W asked that several of their representatives be allowed to fly in the aircraft to observe the instrumentation. Permission was granted and three P&W people came along as observers. The flight deck was quite full with two FTE's, instrumentation, and two flight engineers so we requested that not more than two P&W reps be on the flight deck at one time which resulted in a periodic shuffle of these folks so they could all have their share of viewing. As might be expected the reps were not used to wearing parachutes or sitting in one spot for extended periods so every chance they got they would stand up to stretch and braced themselves against panels and bulkheads.

Shortly after we landed from that flight a Douglas security guard came out to the flight line to talk to the chief flight test rep. They left and shortly they were back and the rep asked to look at the trailing antenna receptacle (the trailing antenna was a thin wire that could be reeled out in flight, if required, as an aid for long-distance radio communications. It had about a five-pound lead weight at the end to help keep it stable while it was extended). The receptacle was empty so the next step was to check on the switch position. It was in the "extend" position, probably bumped accidentally by one of the passengers without the crew's knowledge.

About this time, we began to get a little curious and asked what was happening. The Douglas rep explained that he had been called into the security office to talk to a gentleman who walked in shortly after we landed carrying about 10 feet of antenna wire with a lead weight at the end asking if this belonged to Douglas (since the weight was stamped "Douglas Aircraft Co." it was hard to deny that it was theirs). When asked where he had found it, he said imbedded in the side of his car. He had been stopped at a traffic signal on Lakewood and was watching this "giant" airplane land when he felt his car struck by something and heard a loud bang. The weight had hit squarely on the door-post of his four-door sedan and had caved in the whole side. We understood that Douglas bought the man a new car.

Several days later, Jack Sowers brought in a newspaper containing the news that The Bomb Shelter had suffered a rather large hole in the middle of their roof which they discovered after a rain shower. There were no clues as to what caused the damage.

Now that was a landing

In the C-124A the flight engineers panel faced forward and was aft of a bulkhead behind the copilot's seat. He could see the pilot if he leaned over to his left but could not see what the pilot or co-pilot were doing with the flight or engine controls without leaving his seat.

After a number of flights, the copilot was getting quite anxious to get checked out in the C-124 but there almost always seemed to be some reason why he couldn't conduct a takeoff or a landing. As luck would have it, he was given the chance to make his first landing on a very dark, moonless night. He assumed the left seat and then it was decided that we would get some data for the propeller folks. We were to make a normal landing and then use high power settings during rollout, using braking only as needed near the end of the roll in order to maximize the data time.

I was standing behind the pilots' seats with the camera switch in hand so that I could see to turn on the camera just before the aircraft touched down to ensure that we would get a full set of data. As we approached the runway, I was a little surprised that the copilot had not begun his round-out for landing when Tom Cecil grabbed the yoke and pulled full back on the stick and at the same time shoved the throttles to the maximum forward position. At about that time, the aircraft hit the ground very hard, knocking me to my knees and causing me to lose my headset. While I was scrambling to recover, I could hear Tom Cecil screaming for more power. When I looked at the flight engineer, he had his arms wrapped around the throttles trying to reduce the manifold pressure while screaming that Tom was pulling too much manifold pressure for the RPM. Since both had their mike switches depressed neither could hear the other. Somehow Bill Magruder managed to get the message to the flight engineer that we were not on the runway using reverse thrust but were in the air doing a go-around.

We then completed the go-around and made a normal landing without using reverse thrust. The post-flight examination the next day revealed a permanent set in each wing outboard of the landing gear but it did not appear to affect either performance or handling qualities so tests were continued.

Partially as a result of this incident the bulkhead between the pilots and the flight engineer was removed from later A models and all C-124Cs and the engineer's panel was rotated 90 degrees so that he faced outboard. In this position he could talk directly to and see what the pilots were doing.

A fast hand on the gear handle

As part of the tests being run at Edwards (on what is now called the South Base runway), we were doing a series of take-off tests to determine the speeds that would give the minimum distance from brake release to clear an imaginary 50-foot high obstacle. The ground roll tests showed about the speeds and distances expected but the distance from lift-off to 50 feet was consistently longer than predicted. Captain Cecil wanted to ensure that the contractor could not say we weren't using best effort. He briefed us that on this series of tests he wanted to eliminate the question of delay in gear retraction as being cause for the increased distance. He told the copilot, "Lieutenant, when I say gear up I want to hear that gear handle hitting the up stop before I stop talking." My job was to keep the camera running and hold up fingers in front of the camera lens to mark events such as brake release — one finger, nose-wheel lift-off — two fingers, main gear off — three fingers. Tom would call "brake release" and "nose-wheel lift-off" but then he got pretty busy so I would listen for the cessation of the tires striking the tar strips for my clue that the main gear had lifted off.

We started the series of tests but Tom wasn't satisfied with the results so it was decided that greater effort would be placed on getting the gear handle to the up position faster. On the next run, Tom called brake release and nose gear off so I listened carefully for the cessation of the tire-tar strip noise. At about that time, I hear the "gear up" call and saw Bob move the gear handle smartly to the "up" position — but was still hearing tar strip noise when I noticed the nose gear indicator showing start of retraction. After what seemed an eternity, the tar strip noise stopped and we uneventfully completed the test. Post-flight review of the cinetheodolite film showed the

aircraft with the main gear on the ground and the nose gear retracting.
We ceased efforts to shorten the air phase of the takeoff after that test.

§

The scope of flight testing at Edwards continued to widen. In 1951 the base was designated the Air Force Flight Test Center.

Flight test data was being recorded on board the test aircraft by movie cameras photographing a photopanel, and oscillographs recording continuous-roll strip charts. These records were read manually by engineers or engineering aides, and transferred to 11" by 14" data processing forms. Using a two-foot slide rule, instrument calibrations and various other temperature and pressure calculations were performed manually on each data entry resulting in a final "standard-day" data point.

A two-mile rocket sled track was installed south of the South Base. It used solid rocket motors to accelerate test modules to very high speed, then decelerate them very quickly using a water-trough braking system. The new track was used mostly for ejection seat qualification and flutter tests. Maj. John Stapp endured 45 "g's" while exploring human tolerance to high acceleration using a similar, but relatively short, test track located at North Base.

THE END OF A FLIGHT TEST CAREER
by Richard A. Schmidt

I was assigned permanently to Muroc AFB in early 1950 as Chief of the Performance Test Branch. My boss was Lt. Colonel Jackie L. Ridley who had been Chuck Yeager's test engineer through the envelope expansion and the first supersonic flights of the X-1. Jackie was one of the few Air Force officers who was rated and had a college degree. In addition Jackie had a Master's degree in jet propulsion from Cal Tech.

Only three or four engineers worked for me while we were awaiting the transfer of the Flight Test Division from Wright Field in June 1951. When they arrived I would have 18 engineers working for me.

In April 1951, we were scheduled to test the Northrop F-89A, a two-seater and the Air Force's first jet night fighter. All the test engineers were busy with assignments so I took on the task of flight test planning. I had flown in a number of prop and jet propelled aircraft so I had no reservations about taking on this project.

Northrop F-89A "Scorpion."

Major Mac McAuley was the test pilot and he asked me if I'd like to go to Ontario, California with him to pick up the aircraft and bring it back to Edwards (Muroc officially became the Air Force Flight Test Center and Edwards AFB in April 1951). I had a lot of work to do in the office so I declined.

Upon Mac's arrival and while taxiing to the ramp, the rear seat unexplainably ejected— right up through the tandem canopy! To this day I hate to think what that would have done to me — I probably would not have survived!

I had taken ejection seat training several years before at Wright Field. That too was quite an experience because once you pulled the trigger you knew that you would be shot 85 feet up a retaining slide equipped with ratchets to keep you up there until you could be mechanically lowered. It was also interesting — if not amusing — to watch the facial expressions of the others about to pull the trigger. (They had a look of scared anticipation.)

When the canopy and ejection seat were replaced, we installed calibrated instrumentation and began our flight tests. This airplane was unique in that it had very large split-aileron dive brakes that were relatively three to four times as large as standard ailerons. These brakes were to provide a tactical advantage in dog fights. These big speed brakes allowed the airplane to be pointed straight down at the ground without exceeding the top design airspeed. I was told that you would feel yourself hanging by the shoulder straps. I didn't really believe it but sure enough, I experienced it.

I had experienced pulling a constant 3g acceleration in "wind-up" turns in the B-45 and other aircraft tests but the 7 gs I experienced in the F-89A did me in — and that was 7 gs without a g suit.

I had experienced vertigo in my childhood when riding a roller coaster. I wasn't very old when I learned that lesson and quit riding "amusement" devices that made me nauseated. On previous flights I had become nauseated while flying at tree-top level while calibrating the airspeed system in a light airplane and in the T-33—but nothing like my F-89 ride.

I was so unnerved after that first F-89 flight that I asked Jackie Ridley to relieve me from further flying. Knowing that it would soon become common knowledge that I would not fly, I felt that I could not, in good conscience, continue to assign test engineers to fly when I would not. That convinced me to look for another job.

On reflection, I had a fabulous career in the four and one-half years I was in flight test. I had been involved with the F-82, the Super Connie, C-97A, C-82, and T-29A, and had worked on planning tests of the B-36 and the Spruce Goose. But my involvement with tests of some of the first jet aircraft was the highlight; B-45A, B-46, T-33, and the F-89A — my swan song.

L-19A PERFORMANCE AND SPIN TESTS
by Fred Stoliker

In the Spring 1951 I was assigned as the Project Engineer for the performance and handling qualities tests of the Cessna L-19A to be conducted at Wright Field, Ohio. As part of the performance tests, we had to determine the minimum ground roll during takeoffs and landings on a sod field. The handling quality tests included spin tests which were conducted to determine compliance with the existing spin specifications which called for deliberately entering spins and then determining best control procedures for returning to normal flight.

For low performance aircraft, the normal way of measuring ground roll was to have a number of observers standing on the side of the runway. As the aircraft lifted off or touched down, the observers ran to the spot where lift-off or touchdown occurred. Then a surveyors' chain was used to measure the touchdown/lift-off point from a surveyed runway position. The air distance was determined by the use of theodolites which were spaced along the runway. At brake-release for takeoff, I fired a flashbulb out the aircraft

Cessna L-19A "Bird Dog" following a hard landing.

window and all observers started their stop watches. The watches were stopped as the aircraft passed the theodolite station and I stopped mine at lift-off. For timing during the landing, the pilot would give a countdown on the radio and at "zero" I would start my watch and the ground radio man would shoot a flashbulb which was a signal for all other observers to start their watches. Not very sophisticated and slightly manpower intensive but it worked.

We had done a series of both take-off and landing tests and the data all indicated that the aircraft was meeting its specifications for take-off ground roll and distance to 50 feet but was not meeting either landing ground roll or landing air distance requirements. The decision was made to try the landing tests again and reduce the margin between approach speed and stall speed to 5 knots. The pilot agreed but felt that I should not go along because of the possibility of a stall in close proximity to the ground.

So, bright and early on a calm spring morning the tests were started. On the first approach, the pilot was quite cautious and performed a rather gentle flare. Even at the lower approach speed, the distances were not reduced because of the flare. On the next approach, the pilot made no attempt to flare and hit the ground with a pretty good rate of sink. (The L-19A was built by Cessna and had the spring steel landing gear struts that are still used on some Cessna aircraft.) When the wheels contacted the wet grass at that high sink rate, the sideforce easily overcame the friction loads and the gear just spread sideways. The aircraft fuselage hit the ground with a resounding thump, the struts snapped back, and the airplane was airborne at below stalling speed, so it came back down with another thump. The were at least two iterations of this process. Let me note here that when the airplane made its first touchdown, the observers started running to mark the touchdown point. When the airplane was "launched", they turned and smartly ran in the other direction. However, all was not lost. Each time the fuselage struck the grass, the propeller also hit the grass and left cut marks to mark the touchdown points. This gave us a clear indication of touchdown but it was rather hard on the propeller — the outer fifth of each blade was bent back through about a 75-degree angle.

We ceased all efforts at shortening the landing ground roll immediately. Our report noted that the aircraft should always be flared at landing, especially if the ground was wet.

A former flight test engineer, was in the "Miscellaneous" SPO at that time. When we reported the damage to him, he drove down to the maintenance hangar and had the mechanics remove the prop — on his say-so — and threw it in the back seat of his car. As he went out the gate, a guard saw the prop in the car and asked for his "chit" to take the prop off base. Naturally, he hadn't bothered to get one so they "arrested " and held him. (The guards were quite concerned because they hadn't seen a prop before that looked like that.) When he finally got them to let him make a phone call, all his bosses had gone home. In desperation, he finally got hold of his former boss in flight test who vouched for him. The former engineer, who was newly married, never did convince his wife that the story was true and he hadn't been out with the boys.

After the propeller was straightened and realigned and the engine and airframe checked out, we continued with the tests and started the evaluation of spin characteristics while flying over the south Dayton area. The specification required that spins be initiated in both the left and right directions for various combinations of power and flaps. The aircraft then had to perform five full turns before any corrective action was taken — and the second and fourth turns had to be timed, which was my job as well as recording pilot comments. After a number of spins, my well-known tendency to motion sickness came to the fore. The only handy receptacle was my hat which was promptly utilized and then dropped out the window over a housing development. We then returned to Wright Field where I called for a replacement engineer. That engineer happened to be Jack Wesesky who "never got airsick." They continued with the tests and lo and behold, the pilot got airsick. They landed, called for a replacement pilot, and then continued the tests. Before the tests were finally completed Jack got airsick "for the first and last times" in his career but he managed to complete all tests in spite of experiencing a "first." P.S. I never got my hat back.

While aviation technology was expanding rapidly at Edwards, a more ominous technology was developing in the nuclear field: the first Hydrogen bomb was tested at Entiwetok. The Strategic Air Command needed a long range, jet powered bomber that could deliver atomic warheads anywhere in the world. Boeing's design with two prototypes, the XB-52 and YB-52, made its first flight in 1952. It would compete with Convair's YB-60 as the replacement for the B-36.

AT-6 PERFORMANCE TESTING
by Billy F. Owens

Shortly after my transfer to Edwards in Spring 1952, I was assigned as project engineer for flight test (of all things) of the AT-6 with Chuck Yeager as the pilot. The T-6 was being used in the Korean War as a spotter plane (without external stores at this time), but had never been tested to determine the most effective cruise and loiter speeds as well as maximum load capabilities. The tests were assigned a very high priority. We made many flights every day and the data was being processed on the ground as fast as possible because of the urgent need in Korea.

On one flight, we were doing speed power runs and I was giving Chuck the manifold pressure and RPM setting for each run. As we neared

North American AT-6 "Texan."

the low end of the power setting, I told Chuck to leave the RPM at minimum setting and from there on reduce the manifold pressure. Chuck said we should do the opposite. We discussed it awhile and he finally agreed to do it my way. Paul Bikle later told me that I was the only guy who had ever changed Chuck's mind while he was flying. I asked Paul who was right and he said "You were both partly right."

I still don't know who was right.

DID YOU HEAR THAT?
by Donald R. Smith

In the early spring of 1952 Captain Killian and I were sent to the Martin Company, Middleriver, Maryland to evaluate the English-built Canberra aircraft. Two aircraft had been procured for testing purposes and were assigned to the Martin Company which later built a modified version as the B-57. Flight test personnel from Wright-Patterson AFB were initially given the responsibility for an evaluation; however, an in-flight mishap resulted in the loss of the test aircraft and fatal injuries to the flight test engineer and serious injuries to the test pilot.

We launched into our flight evaluation with considerable enthusiasm. The aircraft had some excellent performance capabilities. It was capable of flight substantially higher than any operational aircraft in the U.S. Air Force inventory. Take-off and landing required relatively short runways; however the single engine minimum control speed was notoriously high.

Martin B-57 with test crew. L to r: Capt. "Buzz" Killian, Don Smith.

44

While the control system was adequate for high altitude operation (for which the aircraft was designed), at lower altitudes and high indicated airspeeds the control forces were very heavy, especially the lateral control forces. The Canberra had a number of pluses and minuses for planned Air Force utilization.

It was while evaluating the maneuvering flight characteristics at high indicated airspeeds that an incident occurred that drew our immediate and complete attention. At an airspeed of around 400 knots and between 4 and 5 g of normal acceleration there was a sudden and very strong "thump" that was both heard and felt.

The pilot immediately returned the aircraft to straight and level flight and slowed down. I asked, "Did you hear that?" "I sure did!" confirmed the pilot. "Could we have hit something— like a...maybe a bird?" "I didn't see anything, not even a feather" was his reply. "Well, if it was a bird it would have been an ostrich, but they don't fly, at least to these altitudes," I commented. "We better go back and land," the pilot advised. "I cannot argue with that suggestion," I agreed.

The control tower was called and told of our experience. As a precautionary move they had emergency vehicles standing by during our landing and taxiing. Visual inspection did not reveal any obvious damage to the outside of the aircraft. We briefed company personnel on what the conditions were when the "thump" occurred. It was decided the aircraft would be put in a hangar and "opened up" so that the structure could be thoroughly inspected.

That evening we paid a visit to the hangared aircraft and were told that the cause of the loud "thump" was determined. The Canberra wing was basically of a single-spar construction with forward and aft auxiliary spars to assist in controlling torsional wing loads. It was the shearing of one of the attachment brackets connecting an auxiliary wing spar to the fuselage that had caused some tense moments for Captain Killian and myself.

That failed wing attachment fitting was made of aluminum. A further investigation into the incident revealed that all Canberra aircraft were to have been retro-fitted with stronger steel fittings. Apparently the two aircraft in possession of the Martin Company didn't have the retrofit. The retrofit was made and our evaluation completed without further incident.

OUT INTO THE NIGHT
E.G. "Bert" Yancey

The trip to Wichita, Kansas from Edwards AFB didn't even start off right. There were three airplane crews (one each for a B-47, C-45, and the B-26) on

Beech C-45G "Expeditor."

board the B-26 when we left Edwards on 30 October 1952. We ran into icing conditions over the California-Arizona border and without anti-icing wing boots we had to turn around and go back to Edwards and change to a B-25. The rest of the trip to Wichita was uneventful.

Major Harold "Buzz" Killian, the test pilot for the C-45 program, and I, the flight test engineer, went to the Beech Aircraft Plant in Wichita to pick up the brand new C-45G for Phase IV performance testing and to talk to the Beech Engineering Department about the differences between the F and G models. The biggest difference was that the F had Hamilton Standard propellers and the G had Aeromatic Full Feathering propellers. In addition, the G had longer wing roots and an increased gross weight capability. After a morning in the Engineering Dept., we went out to the airplane, changed into our flight suits in the plane, and threw our cold weather equipment in the main cabin along with our parachutes. We found that wearing back pack style parachutes made us very cramped in the cockpit. (Killian weighed about 200 lbs on a 6-foot frame and I was about 130 lbs at 5' 5".)

We took off for Edwards via Amarillo, Texas, Albuquerque, New Mexico, and Kingman, Arizona. We stopped in Albuquerque, got a sandwich and refueled, and took off for Edwards. It was getting dark but the stars were shining. We climbed out to 9000 feet, trimmed up, and started chewing up the mileage. Buzz was pointing out some of the landmarks as we went along. He had flown for Western Airlines on this same route in the late '40s and was very familiar with the terrain. About two hours plus into our Albuquerque-Edwards leg, Buzz pointed out some lights about 40 miles ahead on our right (north), and told me that was Flagstaff, Arizona and we needed to climb to 12,000 feet as our new minimum altitude. When he increased the power all hell broke loose. I was looking at the instrument panel and both tachometer needles were oscillating between 800 and 3500 rpm (proper governing speed was 1600-2400). The rate of climb indicator was varying between -2500 and -3500 ft/min. In other words we were going down fast. Buzz hollered at me to "Bail out." While Buzz was making a 180 back to Winslow, Arizona I went back to the main cabin, got on my parachute, and went back to the door. About that time Buzz glanced around and waved me out. I pulled the door emergency release handle but nothing happened. (I found out later that I bent the handle about 30 degrees.) I grabbed a seat back and the bulkhead and kicked the door off and almost fell out in the process. I got back into the proper position and rolled out. As soon as I cleared the tail I pulled my rip cord and the parachute blossomed. When I was about to the bottom of the first oscillation under the chute my legs went through the top of a pine tree — upending me and as a result I landed on my back, stunning me momentarily. I got up, took off my chute, took two steps, and fell over a rock about two feet in diameter (it was dark!) I was right on top of a small peak and I looked in the direction I thought the plane went hoping not to see a fire — I didn't. By then it was getting cold, it had snowed a little the night before and it was freezing where I was, so I went back to my chute and wrapped up in it to keep warm. I decided to stay right where I was until daylight and I could see what I was doing. After wondering what had happened to Buzz I saw some car lights off in the distance, and I watched as they came closer and closer until they stopped about 100 yards from me. Herb Metzger, a rancher who lived about 3 miles south, had heard our engines acting up while he was unloading a load of hay, and then about an hour later he got a call from the sheriff's office to be on the lookout for me. Herb decided to get in his jeep and drive to a neighboring ranch house about 10 miles along a road he and his neighbor had scraped across their pastures so they wouldn't have to drive about 40 miles on county roads to get to each others' place. He decided he would stop and holler each time he topped a ridge on his way — I was sitting about 100 yards from where he stopped the first time. Needless to say, I was glad he stopped.

I left my parachute to mark the spot where I had hit in case we needed to get the planes flight path and went with Metzger to the next ranch house, which was locked, and back to Metzger's where we called the tower operator at the Winslow airport to report the accident. After I got through my short spiel about the airplane number and that I didn't know what happened to the plane after I jumped, the tower operator told me the plane got back to Winslow, and the pilot was sitting next to him — and would I like to talk to him? What a relief. After exchanging pleasantries and how are yous, Buzz said he would arrange with the Sheriff to get me picked up and brought to Winslow that night. Pretty soon the Sheriff called Metzger and arranged a rendezvous about 20 miles toward Flagstaff, from there a deputy took me to Flagstaff where we were met by two deputies from the Winslow office. We stopped at a cafe in Flagstaff for a cup of coffee and away we went at 95-100 mph all the way to Winslow — this was in the days before freeways so we were on a two-lane road all the way. I don't know whether I was more scared from the jump or from the police car ride.

The next day we arranged to get the maintenance officer and our crew chief to fly in from Edwards to check the plane out. After a few anxious moments of the props governing properly when the maintenance officer moved the throttles slowly up and back, he moved them a little faster and reproduced our problem. Buzz and I both breathed a sigh of relief. The crew chief got the proper fluid from Kirtland AFB at Albuquerque to replenish both reservoirs and then everything worked fine. When both aircraft were ready to leave, the Maintenance Officer told me that he had direct orders from the Center commander, General Al Boyd, that I was to fly home in a B-25. So Buzz flew the C-45, without a main cabin door, on to Edwards with both sets of our winter flying suits wrapped around him.

We got a new door and emergency handle installed and flew the aircraft over 100 hours conducting the Phase IV performance tests requested. We were very careful to have both prop systems checked as a standard part of every pre-flight and to only move one throttle at a time in flight. We only had one engine run away (for several oscillations) on us and that was when we were doing sea level power calibrations about 5 miles west of L.A. International Airport and about 50 feet above the water. Needless to say, we broke off our testing and returned to Edwards for more fluid.

I became a member of the Caterpillar Club and my name still hangs in the parachute loft at Edwards. When I jumped the parachute was 7 days overdue to be destroyed because of age. The "D" ring is still in my box of mementos.

§

NACA's High Speed Flight Station continued to push the speed boundary for manned flight, achieving twice the speed of sound for the first time. The flight was flown by Scott Crossfield in the rocket-powered Navy/Douglas D-558 Phase 2. The Korean war ended and aviatrix Jackie Cochran, while visiting her good friend Chuck Yeager at Edwards, flew an F-86 into a shallow dive becoming the first woman to fly faster than the speed of sound. North American rolled out and flew their YF-100 "Super Sabre", the first American fighter capable of flying supersonically in level flight. The B-52 vs B-60 competition began to heat up as the Air Force started its evaluation of the two huge bombers.

The AFFTC had installed an IBM Central Processing Computer which was operating on a 3-shift basis to support comptroller functions and, incidentally, flight test data processing.

C-124C PHASE IV PERFORMANCE AND FLYING QUALITIES
by Fred Stoliker

In spring, 1953, I was assigned as the flight test engineer for the Phase IV performance and flying qualities tests of the C-124C Globemaster II. The project pilot was Captain Wayne W. Eggert, copilot was normally Captain Randy Fetty but others flew in that position, and the flight engineer was Captain Walter W. Whiteside. Nobuo (Bob) Sunada, who was later killed in a B-57 accident along with Andy Hontz, served as an Assistant FTE while working as a summer aide. As was normal for performance tests with piston engines, one engine had extensive instrumentation to measure air pressures around the cylinders and to measure temperatures at the cylinder heads and cylinder bases. On four-engined aircraft, the instrumented engine was the number three engine.

The C-124C resulted from modifications to the C-124A aircraft. The most noticeable external differences were the nose radome for the weather radar and the wing-tip pods containing the heaters for de-icing. Other changes impacting performance and flying qualities were: more powerful (3800 vice 3500) horsepower engines with a manually operated two stage blower; larger diameter, clipped-tip propellers; and changes to the wing flaps and the ailerons. It was still a big aircraft in relation to others flying at that time period.

Douglas C-124C "Globemaster II."

It was still "The Great Aluminum Cloud" and because of the higher power available was even more so "The Douglas Vibrator."

Where'd that bird come from?

As a result of all the high power demands on the engines during performance tests, engine replacements were quite common. An uninstrumented engine could be replaced in a matter of several days whereas the replacement of an instrumented engine could take months because of the required instrumentation build-up — and of course, an instrumented engine was never built up until needed because of the costs.

As you can well imagine, we did lose the number three engine and were down for about six weeks. When instrumentation and maintenance crews said the aircraft was ready, we ran a series of ground checks including running all four engines at high power. When all checked out we scheduled a flight with a takeoff gross weight of 175,000 lbs. Shortly after takeoff, the flight engineer announced that we were losing power on number four engine — torque was dropping rapidly, fuel flow was increasing, cylinder temperatures were dropping, and manifold pressures were decreasing. We turned on the camera to get data while we were feathering the propeller. After we raised flaps and gear, we held a quick consolidation and decided as long as we were airborne we would conduct three engine tests — and so we did for about eight hours. Then, we alerted maintenance that we had "lost" the number four engine and were returning to base.

Upon landing the maintenance crew prepared to replace the engine. After they swung back the cowl flaps and were disconnecting the air scoop to the carburetor, they found an owl with a four-foot wing span spread over the carburetor inlet. He had very effectively choked off the airflow to the carburetor causing the power loss and the strange readings. After the owl was removed, the crew "buttoned up" the cowl, ran an engine check, and pronounced that the aircraft was ready for flight the next day.

The aircraft flew many more flights but we gave the owl a funeral with full military honors. Then we all sat down to work on a keg of beer.

A big ice cube

The C-124C cargo compartment was filled with water ballast tanks that held 50,000 lbs of water that could be shifted fore and aft to control/ change the center of gravity (cg) or dumped overboard in emergencies or to change the weight of the aircraft for specific tests. There was a flowmeter in the lines used for shifting water to control cg but we also had calibrated "dip-sticks" that were used to check ballast tank quantities before and after flights and before and after dumping/transferring any water.

All flights were conducted from Edwards and it was routine to fly tests over the ocean because of the calmer air there. We often flew missions that were six to eight hours in duration where we would take off at 175,000 pounds and then conduct a series of tests while using fuel and dumping/ transferring ballast to attain desired conditions. One day we had conducted a series of tests between 15,000 and 30,000 feet. On the way back to Edwards Wayne Eggert had the co-pilot conduct a series of qualitative stability and control tests at 10,000 feet including power-on stalls — and power-on stalls always resulted in heavy buffeting.

After landing we discovered a discrepancy of about 150 gallons of water between our pre-flight and post-flight dip-stick checks. I was quite concerned about the difference and carefully checked the dip-stick values, but couldn't find the discrepancy. Then the crew chief and I got a maintenance stand and started checking all the dump valves. We finally concluded that the aft dump valve had a small leak and the seal needed replacing.

Several days later one of the Douglas engineers brought in a newspaper clipping showing a car dealer in Long Beach, California, standing next to a car that had the whole top crushed in. The dealer was quoted as saying that he was in his office when he heard a load crash. He looked outside but stated that he didn't see or hear any planes or any unusual noises. That evening as he was closing his lot he noticed the damaged car with a puddle of water in the damaged roof.

I called Wayne and told him of the leak and casually mentioned the article about the car. Wayne said that the co-pilot had been flying a stall test over Long Beach at about the time the chunk of ice descended on the car. We speculated that the water from the leak had frozen on the bottom of the aircraft while we were flying at altitude and then had broken free during the stall tests. We agreed that we wouldn't mention our leaky valve to anyone!

Who keeps blowing that horn?

The C-124 had very noisy hydraulic pumps but they normally couldn't be heard in flight because of all the engine noise. The C-124 brakes were supplied from the ship's hydraulic system— and incidentally, there was a pronounced delay between the time the pilot stepped on the brake pedals and braking occurred. However, when the brakes were applied the hydraulic pumps would almost immediately start up with their high-pitched whine. The sequence, as it occurred, was: 1. The pilot stepped on the brake pedals; 2. the hydraulic pumps came on; and then 3. you would feel the braking action start.

After Bob Sunada had made several flights, he asked me at the post-flight brief one day "Why do they blow that horn before they put on the brakes?" We were all puzzled by his question until we thought through the sequence and then explained it to Bob.

We all then had a good laugh—not at Bob but with him. Thereafter, whenever someone new flew with us Bob told the "horn" story on himself.

"Just call me Red"

During that same summer, we had a large number of summer aides working at the Base and it was decided that it would be a good morale booster and recruiting tool to give them a flight in a test aircraft. The powers-that-be authorized the whole lot — approximately 35 aides — to be flown on the C-124C while we performed an airspeed calibration.

We scrounged around and finally came up with enough parachutes to supply everyone and it fell to me explain how to fit them and how to use them. I assembled all the aides and explained how to adjust the chute harness. Then I launched into the need to carefully tighten the crotch straps before bail-out so that you wouldn't lose any vital parts of your anatomy when the chute popped. At that point, I looked up directly into the face of the only female aide. I felt my face go a fierce red color but she politely smiled and said nothing. However, for the remainder of her tour at Edwards she always addressed me as "Red."

Then off we went into the wild blue yonder. Once we had reached test altitude, Bob went back and told them they were free to roam around the cargo compartment and explained that the F-86 pacer aircraft would soon be off our right wing. We then got busy with our test. About half-way through the calibration the pace pilot let out a yell and moved away from us. The C-124 pilot Captain Eggert asked what was wrong. The pacer pilot resounded "Everyone of your hundreds of windows has got at least one face in it." He soon rejoined us and we finished the test without further incident.

F-94C PERFORMANCE TESTS
by Billy F. Owens

Late in 1952 or early in 1953, I was assigned as the test engineer for the Phase II tests of the Lockheed F-94C StarFire. The F-94C was an upgrade of the F-94B interceptor and two of the major changes were an engine with increased thrust in afterburning to improve take-off and climb performance and a thinner wing than the F-94B. We must have conducted the tests in the winter because I recall that Lockheed had a trailer parked on the flight line adjacent to the F-94C parking area and we would get out of the plane and go into the trailer to get warm. The post-flight de-briefs were conducted in the trailer and were usually attended by Kelly Johnson, Rudy Thorn, and Tony

Lockheed F-94C with test crew. L to r: Billy Owens, Capt. Slade Nash, Maj. Russ Herrington (co-author of Flight Test Manual).

53

LeVier. This gave Lockheed the first chance at de-briefing after each flight.

My first flight in the F-94C was with General Boyd in the front seat. I have always thought they wanted to give this ex-bomber pilot some confidence by having the General make the first flight. General Boyd made his "trade-mark" greased landing to complete the flight. Most of the remaining flights were with Captain Tom Curtis, with Captain Slade Nash making a few.

One evening I was having dinner with Tom Curtis and his wife at their home in Wherry Housing on the base. After dinner, Tom and I were discussing the next day's flight which was to be a maximum speed dive from maximum altitude with wing tanks removed followed by a 3g pull up. As we were discussing this, Tom's wife exploded and asked us to please not discuss this in front of her. She was a very nice person and this, for the first time, made me realize the stress the pilots' wives must be under each time their husbands fly. I was single and had not given it much thought until then.

The next day we executed the dive and registered well beyond Mach 1.0 on the standard airspeed indicator. This did not surprise us because it was inaccurate above about Mach 0.9 and would often register above Mach one. However, when I was later reducing the data to standard conditions and plotting the speed-altitude, the curve showed we had slightly exceeded Mach 1.0. We had an extended nose boom housing and the test pitot tube had been calibrated very accurately. This may have been the first time two people rode past Mach 1.0. I don't know. Later my supervisor made me re-fair the curve among the test points to show slightly under Mach 1.0 because he did not believe the aircraft could reach Mach 1.0. This in spite of the accurate test data.

At the time, I did not care, but now wish that I had taken this issue to Paul Bikle for review.

SUPERSONIC F-94C
by John L. Wesesky

In the summer of 1953, Captain Tom Curtis and I were winding up the Phase IV Performance, Stability and Control tests of the F-94C. We had heard rumors that Lockheed had taken the airplane to supersonic speeds; we were incredulous. The swept-winged F-86 and F-84F could dive to supersonic readily; as a matter of fact the general population was becoming annoyed by the constant booming. A general order was put out that no F-86 or F-84 was to be taken supersonic. So it was decided to see if the straight winged F-94C could be taken past the sound barrier.

An afterburning climb was made to 47,000 feet followed by a 180

Lockheed F-94C "Starfire."

degree turn to head back towards the lake bed. The aircraft was permitted to accelerate to its maximum level flight speed followed by a shallow dive with afterburner to 45,000 feet and then a zero 'g' pushover to a vertical dive. At approximately 37,000 feet the characteristic jump in airspeed and altitude occurred, we had gone through the sound barrier. (Post flight look at the recorded data showed that we had been supersonic approximately 8 seconds.) After the pull-out, we heard a command over the radio for all airborne F-84F aircraft to identify their location. (F-84Fs were undergoing accelerated service tests with a number of them airborne at that time.) Tom reported in that the sonic boom was caused by him in F-94C 962 on a test mission, thus calling off the hunt for the culprit.

Later that day Paul Bikle told me that Colonel Ascani, Director of Flight Test, was conducting a staff meeting at the time of our flight. It was late morning and hot and sunny; the staff meeting room had the windows open with the swamp cooler going and venetian blinds drawn to block out the sun. The force of our shock wave blew the blinds back letting in the blinding rays of the sun along with the sonic boom. Paul said that Col. Ascani hit the deck under the conference table thinking that the Russians had struck with an atomic bomb.

There was a tragic sequel to this event. The F-89D was undergoing a Phase IV test at the same time with Capt. Paul Bryce as pilot and Bill Berkowitz as engineer. It was decided to see if the F-89D, too, could be coaxed supersonic. Because it was now looked on as a hazardous flight, Bill Berkowitz was ordered to monitor the flight from the ground. Paul flew a similar type profile as we had flown several days earlier. The F-89D did get well into the transonic speed range but did not go supersonic. In trying to pull out, however, Capt Bryce found the elevator ineffective and the speed brakes blown back by the high dynamic pressures; the aircraft did not respond to efforts to pull out. Maj. Stu Childs, Chief of Fighter Projects in Test Operations was providing chase to Capt Bryce on this flight. When the F-89D would not respond, Stu called for Paul to bail out. However, Paul waited too long trying to get the aircraft to respond and he went in south of the lakebed with the airplane.

THE GREAT RABBIT ROUND-UP
By E.G. "Bert" Yancey

In the summer of 1953 the Flight Test Directorate at Edwards AFB received a Test Directive from Air Research and Development Command (ARDC) Headquarters to test the first set of all-metal H-25 Helicopter rotor blades in an erosive environment for 20 hours and report the results.

Captain Wayne Eggert was assigned as the Test Pilot and I was the Flight Test Engineer. We had the Ground Crew install and track the new rotor blades and away we went. Our plan was to fly approximately two

Piasecki H-25A "Army Mule."

hours each day for each of 10 days so the ground crew could have the rest of the day to vacuum out the sand and check the wear and tear on the control systems.

The objective of each flight was to go out to Rosamond Dry Lake and hover, or move around slowly, about 5-10 feet off the ground in our self-created dust storm. After about 30 minutes into the first flight I said something to the effect that this sure was a dirty job. Wayne replied "It sure pits the rotors though." About this time a jackrabbit jumped from behind one of the sand dunes and the chase was on. We thought if we stayed in the 5-10 foot altitude we could herd one of those rabbits out to the open dry lake bed, get it to run in a straight line, and chase it to see how fast it could run. The alternate approach was to chase one until it was exhausted. Wayne would set the helicopter down and I would jump out and pick up the exhausted rabbit. Good plan, right? Well we spent the next 19 1/2 hours flying in our own dust storm and eating sand with absolutely zero success.

After the flights were completed we dutifully reported the condition of the blades to Headquarters but forgot to include the results of the rabbit chase—oh well!

YB-60 PERFORMANCE AND FLYING QUALITIES
by Fred Stoliker

In the fall of 1952, I was assigned as the Project Engineer for the Phase II tests of the Convair YB-60 bomber with prime responsibility for the performance portion of the tests. Don Smith (who modestly refers to himself as The Great One) was assigned the responsibility for the flying qualities tests. Lt. Colonel "Danny" Grubaugh, a highly experienced B-36 test pilot, was the pilot, Captain "Fitz" Fulton was the co-pilot, MSgt Harold Ridge was the flight engineer, and MSgt Harvey Cook was the assistant flight engineer.

The YB-60 was an extensive modification of the venerable B-36 aircraft and this modification was proposed as a competitor to the XB-52 aircraft. The most obvious changes were that the B-36 wing had been modified by the insertion of a pie-shaped wedge just outboard of the main landing gear to provide a sweep angle of approximately 25 degrees (the leading edge of the wing inboard of the gear had a "glove" added to provide a constant wing leading-edge sweep angle); the six R-4360 reciprocating engines and the four J-47 jet engines had been replaced with eight J-57 engines in four pods (the same engines and pods used on the XB-52); and because the wing sweep had moved the cg behind the main gear a tail wheel had been added to the normal B-36 tricycle gear.

Convair YB-60.

Part of the preparation for this program was to be fitted with the T-1 Pressure Suit that was anticipated to be required for the high altitude portions of the test program. So off we went to Wright Field — Don Smith and I to get suits for the YB-60 program and Al Phillips for the XB-52 program. At that time the pressure suits were all individually fitted to ensure that they were very snug to provide protection at altitudes above 43,000 feet in the event of failure of cabin pressurization. Once the suits were fitted we were tasked to practice breathing against an oxygen pressure that would be required at an altitude of 65,000 feet. After a bit of practice and lots of complaining, the suits were pressurized so that we got to practice pressure breathing while the suits were inflated. When the suits were inflated, it was very difficult to move your arms and legs, and especially control your arms — the suit tended to raise your arms to a spread-eagle position. The ultimate test to get "certified" was to be sitting in an altitude chamber at 35,000 feet and then get explosively decompressed to 65,000 feet where the outfitting crew cheerily informed us that our blood would boil in a matter of seconds and we would be rapidly dead without our trustworthy suits. We practiced faithfully and after much groaning and moaning about the difficulties of pressure breathing and the pressure exerted by the suits, we all finally succeeded in surviving for 10 minutes of inflated suit and pressure breathing at ambient conditions and were ready for the explosive decompression. (While we were moaning mightily about the pressure of the suits, one of the fitters told us that the pounds per square inch pressure exerted by the suit was less than the pressure exerted by a rubber, elastic ladies' girdle. That shut us up for a while until we had a beer or two and realized that the ladies only had that pressure over a relatively small portion of their anatomy while we had that pressure over our whole body except for hands and feet. It was a real pain in all parts of the anatomy to have that suit inflated and undergo the pressure breathing at the same time.)

Having qualified for the explosive decompression tests, we three were placed in the chamber at 35,000 feet. After the chamber crew was satisfied that we were OK, they punctured a diaphragm so that we were "explosively decompressed" to an equivalent of 65,000 feet. The chamber filled with fog and I felt that I was totally unable to control my arm movements and was trying to hold my arms at my sides. About that time I heard a lot of excited chatter on the intercom. I looked at the observation window through the fog and finally realized that the crew was trying to tell Al and I to get over to The Great One while at the same time there was a great "hissing" of air as the crew started an emergency re-compression of the chamber. I started to work my way over to The Great One and then realized that one of his suit connections had popped open when the suit had inflated. Don was trying to re-plug the hose but because of his suit pressurization couldn't get his hands together to effect the coupling. I finally got to Don but I couldn't force my hands together with enough pressure to re-seat the coupling. Fortunately, between Don and me we were able to get enough pressure on the coupling so that Don didn't "boil away" while the chamber was being re-pressurized. A command decision was made that we had passed the test, didn't have to re-test, and we were sent away with our certifications. We were advised that we had received the number 12, 13, and 14 pressure suits issued within the AF but they wouldn't tell us who received number 13 — I always figured that it was Smith!

Certificates in hand, Al went off to Seattle to join Guy Townsend and Bill Magruder while Smith and I headed to Ft. Worth.

Arriving in Ft. Worth, I contacted Danny Grubaugh. He got me settled into office space and then took me on a tour of the YB-60. The first thing that struck me was that the airplane had both a nose wheel and a tail wheel. Danny carefully explained to me that during take-off roll you basically didn't worry about the tail wheel until you got to a speed where the elevator was effective. The pilot then applied aircraft nose down elevator to take the weight off the tail gear, raised the tail wheel (which had a strut 12-15 feet long), and then proceeded to make a "normal" take-off. When I asked the oft-asked question "What happens if you can't raise the tail wheel?" Danny cheerily answered, "You are then riding the fastest freight train in Texas."

Convair YB-60 with test crew. L to r: Lt. Col. Danny Grubaugh, Capt. "Fitz" Fulton, M. Sgt. Harold Ridge, M. Sgt. Harvey Cook, Don Smith, Fred Stoliker.

(Danny had obviously had a lot of time to practice the answer because he gave the same answer to Billy Owens who a year earlier had asked the same question).

The XB-52 tests were progressing much faster than the YB-60 tests and they soon discovered that the YJ-57 engines had a strong tendency to encounter compressor stall at "low" speeds. This stall was manifested by a very loud bang, a shudder felt throughout the airframe, and a flameout. I was aware of these tendencies both because of Danny Grubaugh's earlier flights with Convair and by staying in contact with Bill Magruder. When we started flying the YB-60, we very quickly found out that we had compressor stall problems almost every time that we departed from a stabilized flight condition — our airframe red line speed was only very slightly higher than the XB-52 stall speed.

On our first flight, Danny invited Don and I to climb out of our "instrumentation cave" while he gave us several demonstrations. The first demo was to show us what happened when you departed slightly from a stabilized flight condition. Danny told us to look at the number seven engine then made a quick throttle movement. This was almost immediately followed by a very loud bang, the airframe gave a kick, and then we saw what appeared to be a solid stream of fuel flowing from the engine until Danny put the throttle into cut off. The second demo was to give a very rapid input to the lateral control after he advised us to look at the wing tip. You could feel the aileron input and then see a "wave" traveling up the wing toward the fuselage. When the wave reached the fuselage it started traveling both forward and aft. When it reached the cockpit we got a rather sharp vertical "bump." Rather disconcerting to say the least.

We flew to Edwards to put the aircraft on the thrust stand. When we landed someone remarked over the radio "My God! They've got wheels coming out their ass!"

We managed to get a total of four data flights before the program was cancelled. None of us involved felt that it was a bad decision to cancel the YB-60 program!

XB-52 PHASE II PERFORMANCE AND STABILITY
by Al Phillips

The Place and Time: Seattle, Washington, Spring 1953 (The mission in this story was actually flown from AFFTC so we could use the lakebed for take-off.)

The Players: Lt. Col. Guy Townsend, Project Pilot; Captain Bill Magruder, Project Engineer and Co-Pilot; me, Al Phillips, Bill's "grunt" engineer (I was 24 years old at the time).

This flight was the second attempt at a range mission and was to be the last flight of the program. The first attempt almost ended in disaster as the turbine on one engine came unglued and the engine blew up just as we rotated and we almost didn't make it. The airplane didn't want to fly and it didn't have any emergency fuel dump system — it was touch and go for awhile. (However, that is another story and not the purpose of this one.)

We lost a couple of weeks while the aircraft was repaired and there was much pressure to finish the program ASAP. The day finally came and we launched on a southbound heading from the lakebed. We were all decked out in those early 50s miserable old T-1 pressure suits and pressure helmets—what a horribly uncomfortable and cumbersome creation to be wearing on a 12-hour mission. In any case, the take-off was uneventful and we were off on our long awaited range mission. For those of you who are not familiar with the XB-52, it was tandem-seated like the B-47 and the test engineers were in a "cave" downstairs behind the pilots. Also, the XB-52 had a dual cabin pressure differential system. The high pressure system gave sufficient cabin pressure that one did not need to keep the helmet face plate sealed at the very highest altitudes. Something was screwed up with the high pressure

Boeing XB-52 and YB-52 prototypes.

differential system so we had to use the low pressure system which gave us a cabin altitude of about 25,000 feet which meant we were on oxygen the whole flight. We weren't about to abort the flight again because of this minor inconvenience.

We no sooner got to our cruise altitude and got things sorted out for our long day's ride when Bill apologetically announced to Col. Guy Townsend that nature called and he had to unstrap himself and get up and go pee. Col. Townsend was not very happy about this. After some grumbling, he had no choice but to concur and Bill eventually got to the relief tube and did his thing. All this time I am listening to the conversation on the intercom down in my "cave" all by myself and the thought crossed my mind that I, too, had to pee. After hearing Col. Townsend express his unhappiness with Bill, I was somewhat reluctant (or to put it another way, afraid) to announce that I, too, had to get all unbuckled and go to the relief tube which was at the aft bulkhead of my "cave." So I decided that I would use mind over matter and I sat there quietly cross-legged for what seemed an eternity trying to convince myself that I didn't really have to pee. It was not too long before I knew that I was losing the battle and I had no choice but to announce that I, too, had to get up and go pee. Needless to say this did not create a very pleasant reaction up front. But after the Boss cooled down a bit he had little choice but to go along with me.

For those of you who have never been fortunate enough to have worn one of those pressure suits, you must realize that with all the wires and tubes that you were plugged into, you were virtually part of the airplane. It was a fairly major undertaking to unstrap and unplug yourself by yourself and replug into the walk-around oxygen and intercom system — remember, we are at about 25,000 feet cabin altitude.

I recall that after getting to the relief tube and starting to do my thing I felt quite light-headed. The next part of the story is kind of fuzzy as I don't remember too well all that took place except that I did realize that I was about to pass out from lack of oxygen. At 25,000 feet you don't pass out near as fast as at the higher altitudes. I recall there was much conversation going on between Bill and Col. Townsend. Apparently I was rather incoherent and didn't make any sense on the interphone and they realized that I was in trouble. Bill wanted to unstrap himself and come down and give me a hand but I

Boeing XB-52 with test crew. L to r: Al Phillips, a Boeing VP, Marsh Mullens, Guy Townsend, Bill Magruder.

guess that Col. Townsend didn't think that was too good an idea to have two of us up and about at the same time. Needless to say, Col. Townsend was thoroughly upset and pissed off at me. The last thing that I remember as I slumped down in a heap on the deck was hearing Col. Townsend's southern drawl, "Let that son-of-a-bitch die."

Though I don't remember it, apparently Bill kept telling me to check my face plate on the helmet (which was unlatched) and I snapped the latch sealing the face plate to the helmet. I regained consciousness in a few seconds and was fine except for my hurt pride and the fact that I was somewhat unpopular for sometime thereafter. When getting unbuckled out of my seat or in unplugging the oxygen or intercom or reconnecting to the walk-around systems I must have inadvertently unlatched my face plate and it took a minute or two for the lack of oxygen to hit me. I guess I wasn't permanently in the doghouse for when Bill went on to bigger and better things Col. Townsend requested that I come back to Seattle a year and a half later and be his project engineer on the Phase IV B-52A Performance and Stability program. We had a great relationship on that program though when we flew high altitude missions and wore the pressure suits, I made sure I never had to use the relief tube. In later years when our paths crossed again, Colonel Townsend was the Wing Commander at AFFTC. I ran Technical Support Division for him and we got along fine so I assume that he forgave me.

If there is a moral to this story, it must be "If you can't handle it on your own carry a clothes pin with you."

AN ODE TO DATA MANAGEMENT
by Richard E. Day

Flight test engineers are a frustrated lot, being confined to writing in the cold, impersonal style of engineering, or scientific reports. Some would like to write in a more expressive form. In the early 1950's the following opportunity presented itself.

I joined the NACA High Speed Flight Station (HSFS) at Muroc, California in the fall of 1951 at the impressive annual salary of $3,100. In 1953 I was assigned to the flight test program of the Convair XF-92A. Although the experimental research airplane was intended to provide data for the delta wing concept, somewhere along the way attempts were made to push the underpowered aircraft supersonic. No matter how hard the pilots pushed and grunted there was no tell-tale jump of the Mach meter needle nor the double bang of a sonic boom on the ground.

In addition to the other advantages of a delta planform, the added distinction of exceeding the sound barrier would considerably improve the image of the aircraft. Consequently, Convair management dispatched their prominent aerodynamicist Dr. G.L. Shue to show the young NACA engineers how to handle their air data.

Dr. Shue spent many hours, to no avail, examining the traces on the film of the airdata instrumentation system, the probe design, its location and any other information that might be gathered to indicate the airplane had exceeded Mach one.

Convair XF-92A.

Being exposed to the volume of data points Dr. Shue had gathered and his arsenal of mathematical tools to massage the data, gave me, the frustrated engineer mentioned above, the opportunity to express my thoughts in something other than engineering "prose." The following lyrics were written, not in elegant form or poetry, but in the unsophisticated form of the limerick:

> There once was a man named Shue
> Who had so many points he didn't know what to do
> So he least squared them all
> And then had the gall
> To fair through only two.

This commentary on data reduction methods had absolutely no effect on the flight test program or its objectives. The XF-92A flew 25 flights between April and October, 1953 making numerous contributions to the follow-on delta wing aircraft: F-102, F-106, B-58, B-70, and perhaps as far down the road as the Shuttle.

§

Lockheed's C-130 "Hercules" took to the air for the first time. An assault transport powered by 4 turboprop engines, it would serve many roles, and would replace the venerable C-47 "Gooney Bird" as the military's "trash hauler."

A new, permanent Edwards AFB began to emerge 3 miles North of the old, and mostly temporary, wooden structures of South Base. A 15,000 foot runway, which emptied onto the dry lakebed at its east end, was completed. Boeing had won the heavy bomber competition. The first production B-52A airplane was scheduled to arrive from Seattle and land on the new runway as part of the runway dedication ceremony. Shortly after touchdown, the rear landing gear truck retracted and the huge bomber skidded crazily to a stop in front of the visiting dignitaries. Damage to the aircraft was minor.

A formal study to automate and consolidate data processing at the AFFTC was completed — the beginning of the end of the two-foot slide rules. The report correctly predicted that flight test engineers would be very upset about losing their data aids. The report also recommended that photo-panels and oscillographs be replaced with magnetic tape recording within five years and noted that an IBM 650 computer was on order.

NACA High Speed Flight Station employees moved into their new facilities at the north end of the new taxiway at Main Base, and on the edge of the lakebed.

Jet engine reliability had improved significantly, and Boeing made the first flight of its "dash 80" prototype jet transport from the Renton Airport near Seattle in 1954. It was the first U.S. jet transport, and would quickly enter production as the Boeing 707.

MURPHY'S LAW
by Donald R. Smith

One of the opportunities that made flight testing at the AFFTC much more than a routine engineering job was that of going along on the test flights to gather data and operate the data recording equipment. Flight test engineers, whether military or civilian, were qualified for flight (as Technical Observers) through physical examinations, special training such as ejection seat and oxygen use, and being provided essential flight gear. Accompanying the test pilots resulted in the flight test engineer having a much better feeling for the aircraft he was assigned to evaluate. However, there were times when I wondered if a more routine engineering job might have been a wiser choice.

One such incident that drew my attention to the risks of flying occurred during flight testing of the Boeing YDB-47E aircraft. A B-47 was modified to carry a Rascal air-to-ground missile. The rather large missile was carried externally on a fuselage pylon projecting down and to the right. Ground clearance of the missile was inadequate, thus requiring the retraction of the missile lower tail fin during all ground operations, including take-off and landing. Retraction/extension was controlled from the cockpit. The "dummy" missile used for the evaluation had the mass and aerodynamic characteristics of the proposed missile.

As was often the case with new weapon-system concepts, such as the YDB-47E/Rascal represented, a short flight test evaluation was conducted by the Air Force to establish weapon system potential and to uncover/verify significant problems. It was one such evaluation that provided the basis for this article.

On the specific test flight when problems were encountered, the flight test crew consisted of an AFFTC test pilot, a civilian as co-pilot, and this author as flight test engineer. The civilian co-pilot was an ex-Air Force B-47 pilot hired by the contractor to be a pilot for future company tests of the weapon system.

Murphy's Law states that "If anything can go wrong, it will happen." That proved to be the case during the latter part of the flight when evaluating handling qualities. A problem first appeared during maneuvering flight testing at high indicated airspeeds. With the aircraft trimmed at 400 knots indicated airspeed (KIAS) the aircraft was slowly rolled into a diving turn to increase "g" while maintaining airspeed constant. As "g" increased it was necessary to increase the dive angle in order to keep from slowing down. Too steep of an angle meant the aircraft would accelerate and gather additional airspeed. This latter situation happened. Maximum indicated airspeed of the B-47 was limited to 425 KIAS because of "aileron reversal" occurring above 440 KIAS. We went above 440 KIAS during maneuvering while the pilot fought to slow the aircraft. He wanted to call for help from the co-pilot but he didn't dare change his grip on the controls as he needed all his strength to recover the aircraft. Luckily, the pilot was big and strong and was able to bring the diving aircraft under control a few thousand feet above the ground.

I often wondered what ran through the co-pilot's mind during the maneuver. He wasn't a trained test pilot and wasn't familiar with test procedures; however, he surely must have been familiar with the B-47 and its flight limits.

The pilot and I were very familiar with an earlier B-47 accident at Edwards AFB that was the result of encountering "aileron reversal." The aircraft hit the ground in a near vertical position and left a head-on imprint in the desert that could be seen from the air for many years afterwards. After that specific accident the "aileron reversal" problem was defined and limits established to avoid the problem.

Not long after our heart-stopper experience the co-pilot requested permission to leave his station and use the relief tube, which he did. To do so it was necessary for him to get out of his ejection seat and stand in the passageway alongside the pilots' positions. When he returned to his seat he announced to the pilot that his parachute got caught on something and deployed. That left no choice but to abort the remaining testing and land.

As the aircraft was prepared for landing, the switch was actuated to retract the missile fin. There was no indication that the fin was safely retracted. After a number of repeat attempts the pilot called for a chase aircraft to confirm the situation. Sure enough, the fin was not retracted.

Operations personnel, monitoring the situation, contacted the Commanding General for a decision on ejecting the missile. The word came back to eject the missile which was accomplished over the AFFTC Bombing Range.

The impact on the overall program of the loss of the dummy missile is not known; however, to my knowledge, little, if any flight testing was conducted on the program after that, at least by the AFFTC. I am sure that the B-47/Rascal Program ended-up like so many ideas, on the junk-pile of never to be weapon systems.

§

The move from South Base to Main base got underway. Reproduction and Data Processing moved before the new engineering building (Bldg. 1400) was completed, resulting in many trips back and forth for the engineers. It was about 10 miles by the outer perimeter road, but only two miles by the old road that crossed the center of the new runway. The new tower was not yet in operation and for a few months the runway crossing was uncontrolled. A sign warned drivers crossing at the midpoint,"Caution, Active Runway - Watch for Aircraft." In an impressive civil engineering operation, two large hangars were moved two miles, across the new runway to their new locations. One would become the Test Pilot School hangar.

The Republic F-105 "Thunderchief" exceeded the speed of sound on its maiden flight. Lockheed's F-104A "Starfighter" was the first production aircraft to reach twice the speed of sound. Still operating at South Base, the Ryan company performed an aerial ballet with their X-13 "Vertijet", a tiny, delta-winged jet that could take off and land pointed straight up, hovering over its own exhaust, then convert to normal forward flight in the air.

Experimental aircraft were using telemetry in conjunction with on-board recording in order to enhance the flight safety decision process.

North American signed a contract to build the next "X" airplane, the X-15.

B-57 FATALITY
by Jack Wesesky

The Base Chapel at Edwards Air Force Base lists the names of all flight test personnel who lost their lives in test aircraft accidents. Those of us who were here at the time recall the details of the tragic accidents which claimed the life of our friends and co-workers. There is one accident that stands out in our memories because it involved the first mission-related flight test engineer fatality since flight test activities had been assigned to Edwards. Test pilot Captain Andy Honts and flight test engineer Nobuo R. "Bob" Sunada were testing the B-57B airplane when it crashed on February 8, 1955 five miles north of Apple Valley, California.

Martin B-57B.

The post-flight investigation concluded that Capt Honts' oxygen mask became disconnected from his supply and he passed out at high altitude. The B-57 had an unusual characteristic when gaining speed —it tended to tuck under at speeds greater than Mach 0.72 increasing its dive angle instead of pulling up. With Capt. Honts unable to fly the airplane, it passed into this tuck region and ended up diving into the ground. Bob delayed a decision to bail out and crashed with the airplane.

Bob was a young (22 years old) flight test engineer who spent one summer working with us as an undergraduate engineering aide and upon graduating from Fresno State College, hired on as a flight test engineer. He had been with us eight months as an engineer following graduation. In this capacity he had assisted Mr. Phillips in the performance tests of the F-100 and Lt. Looney in stability and control tests of the B-57A. He had taken altitude indoctrination at EAFB and ejection seat training at Williams AFB, Arizona. In the fall of 1954 he was assigned as the flight test engineer to work with Capt. Honts in testing the B-57B. Prior to the flight, Capt. Honts instructed Bob on the emergency procedures required in the aircraft.

We can only surmise what Bob was thinking during the fatal dive and why he did not punch out earlier. A little background on Bob gives an insight into why. His family was removed from their farm in 1942 and confined to a detention camp when Bob was 9 years old. After World War II, Bob's father rented and farmed 40 acres near Fresno, California while he was attempting to regain his property taken in 1942. The Sunadas were able to put Bob through college through their meager earnings and were renting a farm at the time of Bob's death. Bob was very intelligent and capable; however, the circumstances of his life had a profound effect on Bob's personality; he was extremely shy and timid.

HOVERING IN THE FOG
by Lee H. Erb

Major August A. (Tony) Vincenzi, our Crew Chief (I am embarrassed forgetting his name), and I were in Oxnard to conduct sea level hovering tests in the H-21C (51-5884). It was sometime in the summer of 1955.

When we got up in the morning the airport was closed to all traffic because of the fog. We were concerned that when the fog did lift, there

H-21C with test pilot Maj. Tony Vincenzi.

would be too much breeze for good data. Tony called the tower and explained our situation. They finally agreed to let us hover between the runways if we did not move without first contacting them. Agreed.

The Crew Chief sat in the left seat taking data and I was laying on the floor with my head out the aft door looking down at the tufts on a weighted string. Maj. Vincenzi had no good visual cues but held a good steady hover out of ground effect. We could see only the ground directly below us.

All of a sudden, while hovering inside the "Dead Man's Curve," we each heard a terrific roar of a multi-engined aircraft as it passed by making an aborted landing. It was a roar even over the noise of the helicopter engine and transmissions. It sounded like it was only about 50 yards away.

Obviously Major Vincenzi called the control tower. The control tower had forgotten that we were between the runways!

CONVINCING THE WIVES OF SAFETY
by Lee H. Erb

After 39 years, this is how I remember it. I hope someone can confirm it.

The XF-104 had arrived for Phase II testing. We had lost a few men in the previous months and the wives were becoming concerned as to who would be next. My wife, Alice, had become used to my flying and was glad that I was flying in helicopters. It is so much safer. (I didn't tell her about the crashes at other bases which caused modifications to our helicopter. Also most of the time we flew without parachutes.)

There was concern about tail flutter on the XF-104 and a rocket sled test of a new tail was arranged for the South Track. Someone decided it was a good time to show the wives how every one was concerned about safety and even rocket sled tests were being used to prove the safety.

The day came and the wives gathered at the South Track. Everyone was to stand behind a concrete wall. The rocket lit and raced down the track. Alice saw something go down the track but never knew what she saw. The wives were immediately hurried to the bus and taken back to the housing area.

Later I was told that the new design had disintegrated part way down the track. Not many of us told our wives about the results of the test!

XT-37

by Lyle Schofield

In February 1955 I had been at the Air Force Flight Test Center for about seven months and was assigned to the Bomber Branch of the Flight Test Engineering Division. The Branch Chief, Donald R. Smith, held weekly staff meetings, but because of other commitments, I missed this particular staff meeting. When I returned to the office later that afternoon one of the office data aides told me that I was assigned as project engineer to an X airplane program. I knew he must be mistaken because I was such a new man and had only one short project completed up to that time. When Mr. Smith returned to the office he informed me that I had been assigned as Project Engineer to the XT-37 program to be conducted at the Cessna Aircraft flight test facility in Wichita Kansas. Needless to say, I was one happy guy.

The Air Force Phase II test program began on 15 Apr. 55 with Charles (Toby) L. Gandy, Jr. as Project Test Pilot. The XT-37, prototype primary trainer, was a twin engine, straight wing, and short aft fuselage aircraft. It had a side by side cockpit under a bubble canopy with conventional stick and rudder pedal controls. Aircraft performance instrumentation was mounted above the glare shield of the right seat and all performance data were hand recorded. An oscillograph was mounted in the nose of the airplane for recording stability data. The right hand stick was removed to allow room to

Cessna XT-37.

73

place an open loose leaf folder with data sheets on my lap for recording data and flight notes.

On one of the early flights we were to acquire stick free dynamic longitudinal pulse data. Toby trimmed the airplane at test point speed and then asked if it was OK to tap the stick to excite a pitch pulse. I said that sounded good and silently thought that this type of excitation would give me a nice sharp oscillograph trace from which to compute damping. Toby "lightly" tapped the stick with his fist and we pulled an instantaneous 5 g's normal acceleration. Since I was bent over a little to record notes, my helmeted head went ZAP on to my lap and the loose leaf note pad, and I felt a sharp pain in my neck. Needless to say we changed our method of doing the stick free dynamic longitudinal pulses for this short coupled airplane. For the production T-37A they lengthened the aft fuselage 22 inches.

§

The rocket-powered Bell X-2 began its assault on the thermal barrier. In 1956 it reached an altitude of over 126,000 feet piloted by Capt. Iven Kincheloe. A few flights later it reached a maximum Mach number of 3.2, but encountered severe roll coupling, tumbled violently and crashed, killing the pilot Capt. Milburn Apt. This ended the X-2 program.

Another fly-off competition occurred between the Republic F-105 and the North American F-107 for a new fighter that could carry a tactical nuclear weapon internally.

In other parts of the world, the super-secret Lockheed U-2 became operational.

HEAVY WEIGHT TESTING
by Donald R. Smith

A request was received from the B-47 System Program Office (SPO) to conduct a 2-flight evaluation of the B-47 at very heavy weights. The test aircraft was assigned for flight test purposes to the Boeing Aircraft Company at Wichita, Kansas. In response, an AFFTC test crew consisting of Major Killian, pilot; Captain Fetty, co-pilot; and this author as flight test engineer was assigned to this evaluation. Contrary to statements made by Mr. Stoliker, the combined weight of the crew did not exceed 700 pounds.

Arriving in Wichita, in January, we received the required orientation briefings and prepared ourselves to initiate the evaluation. Just before we were scheduled to conduct the first flight, a blizzard settled in and stopped all flying activities. The inclement weather lasted all week and confined us to our motel and the Boeing flight test facility. There was a lot of boredom.

Finally, on Saturday the weather was beautifully clear and cold. The test aircraft was parked near the end of the active runway to minimize the taxiing distance and time. The forward fuel tank was filled with heated water rather than fuel to increase the gross weight. The bomb bay carried a 10,000-pound cube of lead-like material. A "horse collar" was fitted to the fuselage and held 33 Assisted Take Off (ATO) bottles rated at 1,000 pounds thrust each. The engine water injection tanks were full as were all fuel tanks. The aircraft weight exceeded 230,000 pounds, a record weight for the B-47 aircraft that was substantially above the normal operational weight. The ambient air temperature was a cold 6 degrees F.

A photo-theodolite was in position to record the takeoff and climbout

Boeing B-47E performing Rocket Assisted Takeoff.

distances. A T-33 chase aircraft was airborne and waiting for our takeoff roll to start. Engines were quickly started and the aircraft taxied onto the active runway. When full engine RPM was obtained on all six engines, water injection was initiated, and the engines started pouring out clouds of black smoke. With all engines running at full thrust, brakes were released and the very heavy aircraft started moving smartly down the runway. The cold weather was really showing to advantage.

At the designated airspeed the ATO units were fired, resulting in a smooth boost in thrust that accelerated the aircraft to and beyond the lift-off airspeed. The aircraft was airborne with considerable runway remaining. The pilot of the T-33 chase airplane, flying close by to the right, was "taken back" by the scene and said over the radio that he had never seen anything like it before. He had never seen so much efflux from an airplane as the heavy black smoke from the engines and the white gasses of the ATO bottles combined to leave a high cloud billowing behind the test aircraft. The horse-collar was ejected beyond the runway, adding the tumbling ATO bottles to the scene. It was spectacular!

The weather remained favorable and the next day we were able to make the second flight. After another maximum weight takeoff we climbed to altitude to link up with a KC-97 tanker aircraft. Starting at an altitude around 25,000 feet, we hooked up with the first of two tankers. As we took on fuel and gained weight it was necessary to increase indicated airspeed to avoid getting into the stall region. The KC-97 was unable to maintain an adequate airspeed in level flight so we were continuously descending. We emptied the first tanker and then hooked on to a second KC-97, all the time descending in order for the tanker to maintain an adequate airspeed. Finally, at approximately 12,000 feet altitude our fuel tanks were full and we broke-off from the second tanker. We had reached 218,00 pounds gross weight, an amazingly heavy B-47!

We could not dump the fuel to quickly reduce the weight so we flew around at high power settings with flaps and gear down, Maximum landing weight was 145,000 pounds, so much time went by before we would achieve the lighter weight. Finally, we made a flat approach and touched down ever so lightly on the runway.

With the second landing we completed our short test program and demonstrated the capabilities of the B-47 at very heavy weights. I do not recall ever hearing of the B-47 being operated at such heavy weights again.

EARLY F-105 LANDING GEAR PROBLEMS
by Bob Hoey

In the 1955-56 time period Republic rolled out the YF-105, a prototype equipped with a J-57 engine. The production F-105 airplane, which was to compete with North American's F-107 and win, would have a J-75 engine. I was a new 2nd Lt. flight test engineer running a 2-foot slide rule and plotting points on green graph paper using orange carbon-backing. The main landing gear struts on the 105 were about 8 feet long which placed the retract pivot point somewhere near the wing tip. During a windup turn on one of the early flights at about 5 g the main gear struts began acting like wing spars as the wing deflected and both up-locks let go. Both main gear extended abruptly, then departed the airplane. The Republic pilot (don't recall his name) made a beautiful belly landing on Rogers lake bed and hardly even scratched the airplane. Everyone was feeling pretty good about the incident when the crane operator, who was lifting the airplane onto a flatbed truck, dropped it from about 4 feet causing serious damage.

A second gear-up landing on the lake bed was made a few weeks later when the gear jammed on another F-105. I don't recall the details of that one but I believe it was the first production airplane with the J-75 engine. The AFFTC performance flight test engineer was Willie Allen (my boss at the time), a guy with a great sense of humor. When we prepared the final Phase II test report we included a plot showing landing distance with two faired lines for "normal braking" and "max braking." Willie doctored up one

Republic YF-105A "Thunderchief."

copy of the report especially for the local Republic folks to review. He had
added a third line on the plot with 2 points on it labelled "gear up." The
politics of the F-105/F-107 competition were VERY tense at the time and I
believe the higher-ups at AFFTC stopped the report before it got to Republic.

That's one of the reasons the 105 was referred to in the test community as the "Lead Sled." The "THUD" moniker originated after the F-105
was in operation.

INTEGRITY OF F-105 DATA
by Jack Wesesky

In the competition between the F-105 and the F-107 for the next ground
support aircraft, the AFFTC conducted what was then known as a Phase II
evaluation of each airplane. Willie Allen was the flight test engineer for the
F-105, but the Test Pilot and Project Officer shall remain nameless. Because
the time constraints for the program were tight, I made a verbal agreement
with Jim Rust who headed up the local flight test engineering group for Republic Aviation to read the photopanel and oscillograph data from Air Force
test flights and provide instrument corrected data to Willie in return for access to all of our F-105 flight test data as it was being obtained, provided that
they did not take the data outside of Republic until our report was published.

Willie was given a desk in Republic's flight test area at North Base to work closely with those reading his data.

The test program was nearly half way finished when I visited Willie to see how his test data processing was proceeding and was amazed to find that he was stymied because Republic was not providing any data processing support. The Republic data processing personnel were working on Republic's home office data requests not his. (Republic's home office was in Farmingdale, NY.) I confronted Jim Rust with this and threatened to withhold all future data from Republic and do our own data processing. Jim assured me that he would correct the matter.

I visited Willie the next day to see if the situation improved and was told that there was no change. In confronting Jim Rust, I was told that the AFFTC Project Officer and Test Pilot had reversed my position and told Republic to continue honoring Farmingdale's requests, that the AF Test Pilot would take the Republic report back to brief on the technical results of the AFFTC tests. I was furious. I went straight to the AFFTC Technical Director, Mr. Bikle, with the situation.

Several hours later, I was confronted by the AF Test Pilot and read the riot act for having him and the Project Officer called on the carpet by General Marcus Cooper.

That afternoon Willie Allen informed me that he was receiving large amounts of data from Republic, that they had turned over their whole staff to providing him the data he needed. Jim Rust told me that Farmingdale had received all the data they needed and he would concentrate in fulfilling his commitment to me.

Several weeks later, as we were reviewing the F-105 Phase II report, the Project Officer came into my office and dropped a large bundle on my desk. It was still wrapped and sealed from the printer's office. The bundle contained Republic's report on our tests. I noted numerous discrepancies, red-lining each to show Mr. Bikle. Two of the most glaring that I recall were that only half of the take-off performance data were presented. Data scatter was eliminated by only presenting the most favorable points. A maximum speed data point of 2.07 Mach number was shown from a Republic flight; the maximum we found was about 1.85. The Republic data point was made on an unusually cold day at altitude, after a diving descent into the jet stream—hardly a stabilized standard day test condition. I was instructed to destroy the package .

The AFFTC F-105 Phase II report written by the AF Test Pilot and Willie Allen based on AFFTC processed data was taken back to the source selection. Although the F-107 had superior performance to the F-105, other factors decided the selection in favor of the F-105. (The F-105 was much easier to maintain; the F-107 had a complex flight control system that was too far advanced technologically for the state of the art and it would have been difficult to keep the airplane flying. The record of the F-105 in returning with battle damage in Vietnam proved the selection to be a wise one in spite of the lesser performance of the prototype.)

F-100C PHASE IV STABILITY AND CONTROL TESTS
by Bob Hoey

The North American Aviation F-100 was the first US jet-powered airplane capable of achieving supersonic speeds in level flight. The F-100 was a fighter with a low, swept wing, configured along the same lines as the F-86, but larger. It was powered by a single, afterburning, Pratt and Whitney J57 engine — the same engine that powered the B-52 (times 8 and without burners). The F-100A was quickly put into production as an air-to-air fighter. The F-100C followed shortly thereafter as a ground support fighter. The primary difference was the addition of six hard points on the wing for carrying various weapons and stores.

I was a brand new 2nd Lieutenant, only seven months out of college. The F-100C Phase IV Stability and Control test program was my first assignment as a project engineer. The airplane was Serial number 54-1744. The test pilot was Capt. Milburn G. "Mel" Apt, although he and Capt. Iven "Kinch" Kincheloe often traded test flights. (Kinch was the F-100C Phase IV Performance test pilot.) The crew chief was Larry Herchkorn, and Joe Ballas was the instrumentation technician.

LABS maneuver in the F-100C
The LABS Maneuver was created in the mid-50's when small, tactical nuclear weapons first became available. It was recognized that a low altitude delivery would place the delivering aircraft in jeopardy unless it could depart the target area in great haste. A maneuver was required which would optimize the distance between the aircraft and the target at the moment of detonation without sacrificing accuracy. For the F-100C the maneuver started with a high speed dash toward the target at tree-top level in military power. Upon crossing an initial point at a prescribed airspeed and distance from the target, the afterburner was lit and a 4 g pull-up was initiated. When the airplane was going straight up (supposedly right over the target) the store was released which produced a long, vertically lofted trajectory for the weapon. The aircraft continued through 3/4 of a loop, rolled 180 degrees, pulled out and departed from whence it came at tree top level and full burner.

North American F-100C "Super Sabre" with special store.

(I don't know if this maneuver has ever been demonstrated with a live weapon).

The weapon was aerodynamically quite blunt and only one could be carried on one wing of the F-100C. The first few tests with the store installed (pulses, level accels, wind up turns) showed some abrupt trim changes due to Mach effects (at about .89), as expected, but they were easily controlled in these test maneuvers. Our first simulated LABS maneuver was flown by Capt. Kincheloe over the Edwards bombing range. I'll never forget his post-flight description of the required cockpit control motions, theatrically demonstrated to all while sitting on the corner of a desk in Test Ops. As soon as he lit the burner and the airplane began to accelerate it began to buffet, yaw right and pitch down from the Mach trim change. At about 45 degrees of pitch attitude, while pulling 4 g, with the horizon no longer in view, it began to decelerate and the trim change reversed itself. Kinch claimed that it would have been pure luck if the airplane had happened to be vertical at the release point and said it was "the worst LABS delivery airplane I have ever flown."

While writing our final report about a month after this flight we received a copy of a report out of Eglin AFB in Florida which stated that the F-100C was an ideal platform and was the "best LABS delivery airplane they had flown." A quick check showed that, while the Eglin pilots were flying the same INDICATED airspeeds, the corresponding Mach numbers AT SEA LEVEL (on the Eglin range) remained just below the abrupt trim change area that Kinch had experienced at 2500 feet altitude on the Edwards range. Our final report explained the discrepancy.

Testing the F-100C for an Atlantic crossing.

In late 1956, near the end of the Phase IV test program, TAC head-quarters decided to ferry a small flight of F-100C's to Europe non-stop. North American had flown some preliminary performance tests on a configuration which used two 450 gal. external fuel tanks rather than the smaller, but more streamlined, 275 gal. tanks that were standard for the airplane. The F-100C had exhibited some marginal handling qualities with blunt stores installed, and the program office felt that a "quickie" stability test was in order. Our airplane was the only F-100C available which was instrumented for stability and control. A letter request came in from the SPO asking for a one-flight evaluation. As I remember we had less than a week to give them a thumbs-up or thumbs-down regarding the ferry flight across the Atlantic. We all recognized that the decision would be made on the basis of qualitative pilot comments since we didn't have time to reduce the data. General Holtoner, the AFFTC Commander, and Colonel Hanes, the Director of Flight Test, de-cided that the flight should be flown by an "old head" rather than one of the youngsters (Mel Apt or Kincheloe) who had flown the Phase IV tests. Col. Frank K. "Pete" Everest, the Chief of Test Operations, was selected to fly the flight.

By now I was a whole year out of college and still pretty awe-struck by the whole flight test business. I was also scared to death of Colonels. I asked Kinch what kind of a test card I should prepare, if any. He said "Just make one up like you would for me. The airplane has a lot of fuel, so there is a potential for a lot of data. If he doesn't want to fly it, he won't!"

I had a pretty good understanding of the airplane by then and put together a rather elaborate test plan. Longitudinal maneuvers were carefully sequenced with the internal and external fuel burn to obtain data over a range of weights and cg's. I had about 15 cards that covered the entire array of stability tests for that configuration, concentrating on those regions that I suspected would be marginal based on previous tests. I had not tried to estimate the fuel allocation during the flight but figured that there were far more maneu-vers on the cards than there was fuel to fly them, even with the 450 gal tanks.

On the morning of the flight, the airplane crew had run into some minor problems and we notified Test Ops that engine start would be about a half hour later than scheduled. When we were finally ready the crew took their tools back into the hangar and I went to the nearest phone in the M & M hangar and called Test Ops. They informed me that Col. Everest had already gone to the airplane. I raced back to the ramp. There was no one around the airplane except Col. Everest. He was wearing his chute, had his hardhat in his hand and was pacing back and forth in front of the airplane like a caged tiger. After he got strapped in I got up on the ladder, quaking in my boots, and explained how to operate the test instrumentation (inserting a lot of "yes-sirs" and "no-sirs" befitting a 2nd Lt. talking to a bird Col.). I then handed him the 15 test cards and started to go through them as quickly as I could, just like Kinch told me. Col. Everest was getting impatient and he cut me off after about 4 cards. He started the engine and taxied out. I walked back to Test Ops to monitor the radio, take notes, and write down counter numbers.

After take-off he called in that he was on test frequency and I acknowledged. That was the only radio call I received on the entire flight. Once I heard him make a wisecrack to another test airplane. (This was before the days of strict airspace control and ground monitoring of telemetry which creates much of todays radio conversation.) After about 3 hours he said he was switching back to tower so I walked out to meet the airplane, figuring that he had discarded my "book" of cards and done his own qualitative flight.

There was a very short debriefing at the airplane. Col. Everest briefly described some longitudinal shortcomings, but said he thought it would be OK as a ferry configuration. He said he would prepare an answer to the SPO. Then, without a word, he handed me my test cards and left. There were counter numbers by every single maneuver! When the photo panel and oscillograph data were reduced I found that he had flown every maneuver on the cards. Some of the static long accels were cut a little short, but the data were excellent. I was able to prepare a follow-up letter with complete quantitative data on the configuration, supporting his qualitative assessment. Needless to say, I was impressed, and I like to think that Col. Everest was also impressed with my flight plan. Wellll...maybe not!

Addendum: On the same day of this flight, Kincheloe was flying another F-100C in an attempt to break some kind of endurance record. He had taken off before daybreak expecting to be airborne for about 10 hours, punching a tanker periodically throughout the day. He had taken along several empty bottles so he could relieve himself over the long flight. At about noon I heard a very quiet, and unidentified radio call on the test frequency, "Bottles full yet?" I recognized Everest's voice. The answer came back, also very quiet and unidentified, but I recognized Kincheloe's voice, "Yep, the next one goes on the floor."

As I remember, Kinch landed early due to an airplane systems problem after a long, but not long enough, flight.

ALTITUDE SEPARATION PROGRAM
by Norris Jay Hanks

Around 1956, there was some thought about increasing the usable traffic density of airways in the United States by decreasing the vertical separation between aircraft at higher altitudes from 1,000 feet to 500 feet. A test was set up to determine the altitude reading errors of all types of aircraft flying airways in the US.

The idea was to ground test and calibrate the existing altimeters and airspeed indicators found in three of each type of aircraft and then to flight test, with a "pacer" aircraft flying alongside, the actual altitude (and airspeed) errors of the three, with the instrument errors corrected out to get aircraft, pitot-static errors. The average of the plotted errors, faired curves of altitude error versus airspeed at each altitude, then were the "answers" for the type.

I had the western half of the U.S., and a large number of military and commercial aircraft to test: Wright-Patterson had the eastern half and about an equal number of aircraft. I flew a C-45 to each test site, such as American Airlines at Tulsa, Oklahoma, with instrument testing equipment, test and repair technician, C-45 and pacer crew chiefs and spare instruments aboard. When we were ready, a pacer pilot, often Don Sorlie, would fly our F-86 pacer from Edwards to some nearby military base, and then, with me in (and often flying) the test aircraft, we would rendezvous to get the pace points at altitude.

Fairly shortly into the test period, a Constellation and a DC-6 collided over the Grand Canyon. Their assigned altitudes were 1,000 feet apart. Eventually our tests of those two types of aircraft showed that they should have missed by a few feet, but with the one assigned the higher altitude a few feet below the one assigned lower — their normal altitude errors were opposite and more than 500 feet at their airspeeds and assigned altitudes.

We found altimeters with gigantic errors, including both erroneous readings of actual pressures and case leaks that made the altimeters read cabin pressure. We found disconnected lines. We found damaged static ports, apparently run into by tugs during towing operations and afterwards causing some very wild readings.

Separate from instrument and system damage errors, we found that normal airflows at design static port locations caused altitude reading errors greater than 500 feet in many aircraft, with some "plus" errors and some "minus". The F-101 was off by more than 1,000 feet under some conditions.

The upshot of the test intended to reduce altitude separations on high altitude airways from 1,000 feet to 500 feet, was an increase in separations to 2,000 feet — a wise move.

In 1957 the technology of flight was dramatically refocussed from "aeronautics" to "astronautics" when the Soviet Union successfully launched the world's first artificial satellite, "Sputnik."

AFFTC telemetry reception and display capability became operational. An Electro-data Corporation (EDC)-204 computer was now being used to support test data processing and reduction. The raw photopanel and oscillograph data were now being keypunched onto IBM cards. The programming instructions for the processing calculations were also keypunched onto cards. The cards were carefully stacked together in the proper sequence, held together with rubber bands, and transported to the central data processing computer. Woe be unto the person who dropped a deck of cards or allowed them to get out of order!

THE RUPTURED DUCK
by Johnny G. Armstrong

All the sawtooth climbs, check climbs, speed powers, and performance take-off and landings had been completed on SA-16B tail number 517200. Now it was time to put it all together in the form of the "Range Mission" and demonstrate the overall performance for an operational mission. It was the morning of 20 May 1957 when pilot Captain Doug Benefield taxied out to Edwards runway 04 for takeoff of this Albatross, modified with extended wings and larger engines. The flight test engineer, Lt Charlie Crawford, was seated at his station in front of the large photopanel ready to hand record some of the flight data. Me? I was a brand new 2nd Lt, on station for less than a year, serving as an apprentice flight test engineer to Charlie (who himself had less than two years of flight test experience). The mission was progressing as planned at the three hour-point after completing several legs of the planned flight track. We were on the leg to Catalina Island over the Pacific Ocean when smoke began to fill the passenger/cargo compartment.

We advised Doug that we had a fire in an electrical junction box on the left side of the compartment. Two of us grabbed carbontetrachloride fire extinguishers and began to attempt to extinguish the fire. We succeeded in putting out the fire at that time, but in the process, created a toxic smoke cloud that totally filled the cabin. We opened the top half of the compartment door, located on the aft left side of the fuselage, and stood at the door trying

JATO takeoff of SA-16B test aircraft.

to clear our lungs while looking down at the ocean below. (We were still at relatively low altitude at this point of the mission.) During this time, Doug had turned the Albatross around and was headed back to the California coastline. We were approaching the coastline with things calming down, giving the impression that we were home free,when.....KABANG!! The junction box exploded, deforming the cover. At that point, Doug shutdown the left engine, feathering the prop, hit the gear down switch and set up for an emergency landing on the beach. When it was apparent we were going to make an emergency landing we sat down facing aft with our backs against a seat. Very quickly we hit the sand, bounced back up in the air, and hit again coming to rest in the ocean about 300 feet off the shore. We climbed out of the aft side door and proceeded to wade to shore in waist deep water — me with my orange covered Herrington Flight Test Manual in my hand. We (about 7 total onboard) stood there looking at the results of our handy work on Sunset Beach, 5 miles south of Long Beach. The gear was still in the process of extending when we hit and one of the main gear was ripped from the aircraft and lay on the beach.

The bottom of the aircraft was sitting on the sand parallel to the beach in shallow water. It was being rocked in the roll axis with each wave causing the float on the right wing to collide noisily with the sand. Surf fishermen, who had long since thrown down their poles and scattered, were beginning to wander back to the crash site. So, in a group, we wandered toward the nearest beach house to be greeted warmly by the very pregnant occupant. She invited us in and Doug Benefield called Edwards and broke the news to them. Meantime our host had gone out and returned with a six pack of beer that she offered to her surprise guests. We all thought, under the circumstances, we best decline. Eventually, the H-21 helicopter from Edwards arrived. I can still see the flight surgeon, even now, as he came walking up to us with his little black bag marked "Human Remains." We arrived back at Edwards and were taken to the hospital for observation. We all checked out OK except for a few of us that had some problems from breathing the carbontetrachloride/smoke.

As I was walking to my room in the BOQ, still in my wrinkled flight suit and with my wet Herrington manual in my hand, my close friend, Rob Ransone, made some snide remark like "What have you been doing? You look like you have been in an accident!" He came close to getting clobbered. The next day, the LA Times showed a large photo of the airplane on the beach and the broken landing gear in the foreground with one inch headlines on page 1; "Big Rescue Plane Rests in Surf After Forced Landing on Beach." My log book shows 4+10 of SA-16B time and 1+15 of H-21 time on 20 May 1957. I qualified for my flight pay that month.

TINY MODELS THAT FLY LIKE THEIR BIG BROTHERS
by Bob Hoey

In 1957 I was the Project Engineer on the Phase IV Stability and Control test of the F-104A. Several of us young AFFTC engineers were also building free flight model airplanes and competing (usually unsuccessfully) in nearby contests on weekends. When the small Jetex solid-rocket motors first came on the market, I thought it might be fun to build a free flight scale model of an F-104A powered by one of these little rockets. My first concern was spiral stability with that 10 degrees of anhedral (negative dihedral) in the wing. I cut a side view profile of the F-104A out of thin balsa, then cut the planform shape of the wing and glued it on with the appropriate minus 10 degrees of dihedral, then the horizontal T-tail. The model was about 8 inches long. I added clay to the nose and was soon gliding the model around the living room. It flew great, and appeared to be spirally stable — the T-tail apparently overpowering the negative dihedral. In fact, it flew TOO GOOD! I knew that the F-104A exhibited a severe pitchup when it stalled, and my model had a normal and gentle stall. I added some additional wedge-shaped balsa pieces to the side of the fuselage to duplicate the planform shape of the forebody and engine inlets. The model still flew very well at normal speeds, but when launched slightly upward, it slowed down and exhibited a couple

Bob Hoey with model gliders.

of cycles of "wing-rock", followed by a severe pitchup. It looked just like the movies I had seen of the on-going spin program being flown by Virgil Givens on the F-104A at Lockheed. I demonstrated the model to some of my fellow engineers at the office and they were suitably impressed.

Feeling the elation of success, I built a similar model of the F-101A which also had a T-tail and was known to have a pitchup. Sure enough, my model showed the same characteristic. Next was a model of the F-100 which I knew did NOT have a pitchup, and — success again! I eventually built models of the X-15, F-102, F-84 and even the B-58, (although the office furniture kept knocking off the pod-mounted engines). All showed stall characteristics similar to their much larger counterparts. T-tails showed pitchup characteristics, delta wings showed slight wing-rock and high descent rates. Since some of these configurations were still classified at the time (F-104, X-15, B-58), I watched all of the aviation magazines for the 1st publication of a 3-view so I could build the model at home in good conscience.

Word got around fast in those days, and I soon found myself demonstrating the models to Paul Bikle, the AFFTC Technical Director. Shortly after that, I got a call from his office asking me to bring the models down to Base Ops. When I got there I found Mr. Bikle and General Boyd (who had just arrived for a short stopover), and several other AFFTC staff members. Within a few minutes all of the "brass" were acting like a bunch of kids, gliding these little models across the waiting room at Base Ops. A good time was had by all!

Addendum: I did build a larger (23-inch) F-104A model in 1957 using a Jetex rocket, but it was woefully underpowered. I only had a few short flights before I stored it away in my garage. In 1992, 35 years later, John Manke and I made several successful free flights on this same model by air-launching it from a large radio-controlled model airplane. Trimmed for a normal glide, the model was stable and graceful in flight. When trimmed into a stall, the model showed the same wing-rock and pitchup characteristics as the real airplane, and usually the same oscillatory spin characteristics. On several occasions we have seen the non-oscillatory "deep stall" mode which caused Chuck Yeager to bail out of the NF-104 in 1963.

YC-134 - ONE VERY SHORT FLIGHT EVALUATION
by Charles A. Neyhart, Maj. USAF (Ret.), Charles Kroll, (then)Lt. USAF

The YC-134 was built by Stroukoff Aircraft and designed by (don't remember first name) Stroukoff, a White Russian, who had been chief design engineer at Chase Aircraft before it became Fairchild Aircraft. He left Chase Aircraft over a dispute about using the dorsal fin on the C-123 as the method for directional stability, and formed his own company. The YC-134 aircraft was a medium weight cargo aircraft powered by two Pratt & Whitney R4360 engines, new wings for STOL operations and a sealed fuselage. It was equipped with combination wheel and ski landing gear. This was a true pantobase aircraft that was designed to takeoff and land on dry land, ice, snow, or water. The aircraft was completely instrumented, had a YAPS head on a boom, and a photo panel and oscillograph in the aft fuselage. As we recall, Stroukoff was attempting to compete with Fairchild's C-123J as a medium weight cargo transport for land and snow operation. Stroukoff had included a Lockheed "CONNIE" Constellation tri-tail which had a large center vertical stabilizer and a smaller vertical stabilizer at each end of the horizontal stabilizer for directional stability.

On 1 March 1957, Major Jones Siegler, test pilot; Captain Charles Neyhart, co-pilot; and Lieutenant Charles Kroll, flight test engineer, went to Stroukoff Aircraft Company in Trenton, New Jersey, to do a preliminary Air Force evaluation of the YC-134 aircraft.

We were to make the first flight on 2 March, which would be a checkout flight for Maj. Siegler. By the time we had pre-flighted the aircraft and studied the handbook, it was late afternoon. As we took off, a snow storm hit the area, so it was a tight pattern, around the field, and in to land. Upon landing it felt like the left gear had collapsed as we veered off the

Stroukoff YC-134.

runway. Contractor personnel came running out of the hangar. When they saw there was minimal damage to the plane they insisted that they would have it fixed in two or three days. It was a smooth landing, but faulty design of the landing gear. The landing gear had a three position control of UP/ SKIS-DOWN/WHEELS-DOWN. In the WHEELS DOWN position the skis came down and then slightly retracted so that the wheels extended slightly below the skis. During the landing it appeared the gear had operated correctly, but after touchdown the skis had not stayed retracted and extended down and contacted the concrete which tore off much of the Teflon skin. We recall their description of the event mostly because of Mr. Stroukoff's comment in his native European accent, "Next time vee make dem out of schteel."

The "two or three days" became 16 days and our next flight was on 18 March. We made other flights on 21, 22, and 23 March. It was the last flight that gave us gray hair. We were in the Delaware River area and were working on accelerated stalls. The aircraft had an interior fuselage test configuration with the oscillograph on a table and a photo panel at engineer's eye level and an engineer's seat. The photo panel and engineer's station were enclosed with a black curtain to prevent sunlight from causing glare on the photo panel film. However it also prevented the test engineer from having any outside visual reference. Lt. Kroll had given Major Siegler the trim conditions for the stall entry, and wanting to be sure he was ready for the next test point, was looking at the flight cards rather than the instruments in the photopanel. After what seemed a reasonable length of time, he called Major Siegler on the intercom to give him the trim conditions for the next test point. Major Siegler, being the calm, cool and collected test pilot that he was, replied, "If it's all the same to you Charlie, I'd like to get us out of this maneuver before we think about the next one." Puzzled, Lt. Kroll looked at the photo panel and noticed altitude decreasing which meant we hadn't recovered yet. But his concern increased when he saw the airspeed indicator reading its minimum value of around 43 knots. Being inside the black curtain, Lt. Kroll had no outside visual reference and hence was not aware of the nose high aircraft attitude. About that time he felt and could see engine instruments indicate power being added on one engine. Altitude continued to decrease but airspeed increased and we finally recovered from a deep—very deep—stall, coupled with a rudder lock condition. Since control positions and forces were on the oscillograph they couldn't be observed at the time. Later we read the records and analyzed that Jones had used all the directional control that the "CONNIE" tail provided plus asymmetric engine power to literally turn/yaw the aircraft to a nose down attitude in order to regain flying speed. The maneuver had been very benign as far as acceleration in any axis. The aircraft just proceeded into the stall, but instead of making a nose down recovery as called for by Mil Spec, remained nose high, decelerated, lost altitude and just stopped flying. The yaw and pitch readings were bizarre with 90 degrees of yaw being indicated at times. There was little or no elevator control, at least insufficient to pitch the aircraft nose down. Later Major Siegler said that if his engine powered directional control attempt hadn't worked, his next command would have been to the crew instead of the aircraft, namely to BAIL OUT.

We returned immediately to the field, landed and advised Mr. Stroukoff that the Air Force flight evaluation was terminated. We returned to Edwards with the data and the Air Force never evaluated the YC-134 again. Our instrumentation readings were used in the Test Pilot School on the final stability and control exam. The question was, "Explain what happened in this flight test maneuver?"

Back on the ground, we questioned the company pilot as to why he had not told us about the accelerated stall problem. He confessed that he broke the right landing gear in the test program, which had put them three weeks behind, and they had not done any accelerated stalls thinking there would be no problem.

Needless to say, the Air Force did not buy this aircraft!

(Editors' note: This story was originally submitted separately by the two authors. There were differences in the two versions of the event. After exchanging each other's stories, this "co-authored" version was prepared.)

HILLER HORNET
by Jim Hayden

My first contact with the Hiller Hornet was in 1957 when an Army YH-32 arrived at Edwards Air Force Base for Performance and Stability testing.

Early in WWII a very bright high school student in Palo Alto, California had a dream about putting a small helicopter in every household as a means of alleviating traffic congestion and improving the quality of life. In 1941 Stanley Hiller formed Hiller Aircraft Co., a division of the family owned Hiller Industries. By the early fifties Hiller had built several types of rotorcraft including one with two seats powered by one ramjet on the tip of each of two rotor blades. Since the rotor was tip-driven, there was no requirement for directional anti-torque (only for directional control) and it was equipped with a one-bladed 1 1/3 ft. radius tail rotor that was driven by a fan belt from the main rotor.

Almost everything about this aircraft was "funny" or very different. The YH-32 arrived in early 1957 and had been tested for service suitability by the Navy at Patuxent River Maryland, by the CAA, and by the Army at Ft. Rucker Alabama. Capt. Bill Lake was assigned as test pilot, I was assigned as project engineer and Sgt. Buckley as crew chief. Bill was an outstanding test pilot and also had the distinction of being the lightest helicopter pilot in Cargo Miscellaneous Operations. Previous testing had all been conducted at

Hiller YH-32 "Hornet."

sea level and we expected the performance to be marginal at 2250 feet but found out that it was almost non-existent. Weight was very important. It was obvious from the start that my flight test engineering would be done from the ground. There was physically no room in the cabin for both me and the instrumentation, and also performance would not allow the weight of both.

Minimum instrumentation was installed, and to balance the lateral center of gravity we had to mount the instrumentation battery externally on the skid tubes. With full fuel, 50 gal., the aircraft would not begin to hover so we installed four wheels (like from a grocery cart) on the skids so we could make running takeoffs. We did our "up and away" flying from the Weight and Balance Hangar and used the tower-to-NACA (remember that at this time Sputnik was still a few months away) taxiway for running takeoffs when we had burned enough fuel, and for landings, well into the low fuel warning to get the last data point.

We flew at night on the ramp behind the Test Pilot School and the vertigo from the beautiful blue-yellow flame halo was incapacitating to us on the ground as well as to the pilot.

The noise levels were horrendous. Noise was not taken seriously in those days (except for the supersonic prop-equipped XF-84H which stopped all useful activity at Edwards whenever the engine was running). We measured 101 db at 500 feet and 131 db at 25 feet. This testing undoubtedly contributed to my wearing a hearing aid today.

By today's standards the aircraft was an environmental disaster. Starting was accomplished by the crew chief holding a 2 1/2 hp two cycle engine, belching gobs of black sooty smoke, to get the rotor turning fast enough to get a shock wave in the ramjets. When you turned on the fuel, a cloud of atomized gas enveloped the aircraft and anything else in the vicinity. Because of the very high drag of a flamed out engine, both engines had to light to accelerate the rotor. The engines were very sensitive to airflow and flamed out quite often. They usually relighted quickly but you were subjected to periodic dousing with atomized gas in addition to carbon monoxide from the inefficient combustion. The rotor system had very high relative rotor inertia but the sensitivity of the engines to changes in airflow (rotor speed) completely negated the pilot's ability to use the rotor inertia to help fly the aircraft.

The most frightening characteristic of the aircraft was engine-out performance. The ramjets were terribly unreliable and the high skid gear plus the added height supplied by those wheels made the system top heavy, a set-up for rolling up in a little ball on an autorotational landing. Ramjet drag when an engine flamed out (Cold Drag) was greater than the thrust when it was running. We tested the one and two engine-out performance over the

93

Edwards main runway complete with firetrucks, ambulance, Askania takeoff cameras and movies. Bill had a cutoff switch so he could kill and later restart the engines. We successfully measured the one-engine-out rate of descent at 2280 ft./min. and the autorotational rate of descent at 3450 ft./min.; more than double what was common in those days. Luckily, Bill did not have to complete the landing in autorotation. This was the only time I know of when a helicopter has closed the main runway at Edwards.

We reported that, in addition to the problems mentioned, the aircraft failed to demonstrate, even at very short ranges, the high useful-load to empty-weight ratios claimed by tip propulsion proponents of the day. Fuel consumption was approximately twenty times that of a typical shaft driven, turbine powered helicopter. The Army had purchased five airframes for research and development evaluation and, like the proverbial "old soldier", the YH-32 did not die — it just faded away.

YB-58 PHASE 2 TESTS
by Johnny Armstrong

The Phase II designation in the Air Force's test syllabus in 1957 was the first Air Force evaluation of an aircraft following the "contractor only" Phase I test program. The first two four-engine supersonic Convair B-58 bombers were given the "Y" designation, indicating the aircraft were considered prototype aircraft (a notch above being experimental). It was a sleek and exciting aircraft for its time with four afterburning GE J-79 engines mounted on pods on the highly swept delta wing. The aircraft was designed to have a Mach 2 dash capability to and from the target area dropping the large externally mounted bomb pod which also doubled as a fuel tank. To optimize engine performance above Mach 1 the engine installation included moving nose cones in the inlets to position the shock wave for optimum air flow to the engine.

Here I was a "still green behind the ears", 24 year old 2nd Lt at the Convair plant in Fort Worth, Texas, after having put on my gold bars only a year prior and reporting to Edwards. I was an apprentice flight test engineer assisting Ev Dunlap along with the pilot, Capt Fitz Fulton, and crew chief, M/Sgt Cliff Garringer. We were here to conduct the Phase II performance and stability and control tests on YB-58A S/N 55-661, the second aircraft off the production line sporting a bright red painted nose, wing tip, and vertical tail with accenting white diamond streaks. It looked fast just sitting on the ramp. The flight test engineer's station was the second of three tandem flight stations. It was equipped only with an eight day clock, airspeed indicator, an

Convair YB-58 with test crew. L to r: Johnny Armstrong, Maj. "Fitz" Fulton, M. Sgt. Cliff Garringer, Everett Dunlap.

altimeter and the data management system panel. It also had 60 removable type fuses right on the forward panel. Only a small peep hole measuring about 5" by 10" on each side of the hatch gave the engineer a very limited view to the outside world.

During the early testing days of the B-58, the General Electric J79-7 engine was new and lacked reliability. It consumed a lot of oil and was subject to excessive vibrations. One of my duties was to routinely monitor the measured vibration level of each engine. It seemed to be routine to end up shutting down an engine during flight for one of the above two reasons. The additional problem that 661 had was Jinx Armstrong. Seems like every time we were scheduled to conduct tests at Mach 2 something happened along the way and we terminated the flight before getting to the Mach 2 test point. The Convair crews began to refer to me as "The Jinx." I sorely wanted to make it to Mach 2.

The morning of 25 February 1958 Fitz taxied 661 out to the north end of the Carswell AFB runway and I could barely see Lake Worth out the small window as he turned the aircraft facing south. Another noisy, pushed-back-in-the-seat, burner take off, a wide turn and we were headed outbound. Our acceleration toward Mach 2 was going good and we were almost there....then it happened. The aircraft started vibrating intensely accompanied by lots of metal rattling noise and I found myself being pushed to one side. About that time Fitz radioed over the intercom in a grunting voice, "Johnny get the data on." I threw the data tape switch on and my next step was to clean up my station to get ready to leave it. I had a fold down table over my lap that I used for recording data. It had to be stowed before I could eject and believe me I started getting ready. The outboard #4 engine had encountered what I now believe to be an unstart. In those days I did not know about such things. When the shock wave from the engine nose cone is not at the proper position the engine regurgitates the airflow back out the inlet producing a large amount of drag. Finally as the aircraft decelerated things quieted down and we were headed back to Carswell with the #4 engine shut down. It was now just another RTB with less than our full complement of thrusters. Then in a typical Fulton calm radio call he announced he was shutting down the #1 engine due to low oil.

So now we were slowly descending through 25,000 feet on two engines. Soon Fitz radioed in an observation tone that we were passing a B-47 heading in our direction. Finally the flight ended routinely and once again Jinx got the wrath of the Convair team members. Several days later the Fort Worth Press came out with headlines in boldface on page 18, "B-58, TWO ENGINES OUT, PASSES B-47!" The report stated: "A Convair B-58 with two engines out breezed past a cruising B-47 Stratojet last week, THE PRESS learned yesterday. The incident happened Tuesday near Oklahoma City. The B-58, being flown by an Air Force pilot, was 'limping' along with only two of its four General Electric J-79 engines in operation. It was not clear whether the engines went out or were deliberately shut down in a test. At any rate, the Convair plane easily overtook and passed a B-47 Stratojet flying the same course. The B-58 pilot almost came unglued with excitement, THE PRESS was told." Fitz, unglued....Ha! Never! Now, to appreciate THE PRESS story you need to understand that Fort Worth folks were not too fond of Boeing and its flying machines ever since the Boeing B-52 won over the Convair YB-60.

Now it was 3 March 1958 and Jinx was airborne again in 661. This time he made it to Mach 2. After the flight the Convair crew made a big to-do over it presenting me with a two dollar bill with my picture pasted in the center and signed by all the crew associated with 661. Later at a dinner ceremony of the Mach 2 Club I received my Mach 2 pin and Mach 2 card #24 signed by B.A. Erickson, who was Convair chief pilot at the time. Jinx may have been the first non-rated Air Force officer to fly to Mach 2.

YF-104B
by Fred Stoliker

I ALMOST made it to Mach 2!

Lt. Russ Myer was conducting tests on the YF-104B and he came by one day and offered me a "nice" ride in the YF-104B—- there were no tests involving aileron rolls or pulling g's, and an opportunity to get to Mach 2 - just some dynamic lateral-directional tests. (Russ was well aware of my queasy stomach and he was really setting me up for a soft ride.) The test card called for an afterburner climb to 35,000 feet and then accelerating to Mach 2. Every 0.1 Mach, the pilot was going to hit the yaw damper "hardover" switch to excite the lateral-directional mode. All I had to do was turn the instrumentation on and off and record counter numbers.

During my pre-flight brief, Bob Hippert, the pilot, said "If I tell you to punch out, don't say `what?' cause there won't be anyone there to answer." That was my first clue that this might not be a "routine" flight.

Off we went! Afterburner takeoff and climbout were most impressive. As we leveled out at 35,000 feet, we were flying parallel to a very dark contrail and I asked Hippert why it was so dark. He responded that it was a fresh one.

Tests went along nicely. Bob alerted me when to turn the instrumentation on and off. As we passed 1.9 Mach, he alerted me that he was going to throw in an extra test because the airplane was a little "loose" at the last point. Just after he hit the hard-over switch, there was a loud bang, and I found myself thrown forward, hanging in the shoulder harness. My first thought was that we had hit whatever was making that fresh contrail. It was awfully quiet and there seemed to be quite a Dutch roll!! I could see Hippert was still there so I knew I wasn't alone.

After things calmed down Hippert commented that we had a duct "unstart", causing a strong Dutch roll, and the afterburner had blown out resulting in the rapid deceleration that put me into the shoulder straps.

As a result of these tests a "duct-splitter" was installed in all YF/F-104's to inhibit the unstart condition during sideslips and/or Dutch rolls.

Never did get to Mach 2— only 1.94 — and never got a Mach 2 pin! However, I made sure to thank Russ for my "nice, quiet" ride and I didn't have to use my ever-present "urp" bag.

§

In 1958 President Eisenhower responded to the Soviet "Sputnik" by establishing the National Aeronautics and Space Administration (NASA), using the NACA as the nucleus for the new organization. Shortly after formation of the new organization the U.S. launched its own artificial satellite, "Explorer I."

The North American X-15 arrived at Edwards.

An IBM-704 replaced the EDC-204 computer for data processing at AFFTC.

IT WAS NOT MY TIME
by Rob Ransone Copyright © 1995 Ransone Associates, Inc.
Used by permission

The closest call I had during my entire career at Edwards was for a flight that I was not on. The week before Christmas, in 1958, I needed four hours flight time to get my hazard pay for the month. We poor Lieutenants needed every dime we could get, even though we lived in the BOQ and ate in the Officers' Club. Some of us bought TV dinners, and heated them in our bathroom sinks by running hot water over them for a half-hour. This worked fine, unless there was a small hole in the aluminum foil covering — then we dined on meat loaf soup, fried chicken soup, or roast beef soup! It was a month before Paula and I were to be married, and I needed the money. So when I found that Bob Williams had the back seat open on a B-57 Canberra, I asked for a ride, and he said OK.

Just before lunch, I went to Test Ops and got my chute and helmet, and was waiting for Bob at the dispatch desk, when Col. Lane, Chief of Test Ops, came by. We chatted for a while, and then he asked me what I was flying. "The B-57, with Bob Williams," I answered. He thought for a moment. The Canberra was a twin-engine British medium bomber, designed to the British vertical tail criteria of engine out with the remaining engine at idle power, instead of the US criteria of maximum power on the remaining engine. This made the Canberra's vertical tail smaller, for less drag, but it had nasty lateral-directional characteristics with one engine out. "That's a pilot proficiency check flight," Col. Lane said. "Maybe you shouldn't go on that one."

For some reason, I wasn't really anxious to fly that day, so I said OK, turned in my flight equipment, and left Bob a note that I wasn't going with him. I had lunch at the Officers' Club, got a haircut, and returned to the office about 1 o'clock.

When I walked in, everyone looked at me like they were seeing a ghost.

"We thought you were on that B-57!" they exclaimed. "I canceled, why?" They pointed out the window to the main runway, where an ominous column of black smoke was still rising.

"Bob Williams flipped upside during a single-engine go-around practice. He was killed."

A "SIMULATED" ENGINE FAILURE
by Fred Stoliker

Somewhere around 1958, performance and handling qualities tests were being conducted on the Kaman H-43 (the H-43 had twin, side-by-side rotor blades mounted on side-by-side pylons. The rotors meshed as they rotated—naturally this soon led to the slang description of "inter-smashing" rotor blades. Because of the counter-rotating blades no tail rotor was deemed necessary for directional control, but the manufacturer had added many vertical fins to the helicopter). The standard tests included "chopping" an engine to simulate engine failure and then evaluating the handling qualities during the transition to autorotational flight, determining the autorotational rate of descent, and then the handling qualities during the transition from autorotation to landing. The pilot was Captain Jimmy Honaker, a very capable and experienced helicopter test pilot, and the test engineer was Ken Ferrell, a young but eager and determined engineer.

After the first simulated engine failure, Captain Honaker reported that there was an excessive nose-down pitching moment. I asked him what he meant by "excessive" and he immediately replied "too much" — so, of course, I asked what's too much. After several iterations of questions and answers, he said come on and see for yourself. So, I put on my trusty flight jacket and we headed out in the H-43 for the south lakebed.

As we approached 5000 feet, Captain Honaker said that he would level off, get everything stabilized, chop the throttle to idle, and then set up an autorotation. My plan was to watch the engine rpm until it started to decrease and then switch my attention to his hands and feet to watch what kind of inputs he had to make. Jimmy set up everything and asked if I was strapped in tightly and I replied yes. He said here we go! Sure enough the engine rpm started to bleed off, but quite slowly. I was intently watching his hands and feet. I didn't see any large amounts of control action and then I became aware of a "Mayday" call from someone over the south lakebed. I turned to look at Jimmy's face and realized that he was the one making the call. I looked at the rotor rpm and it was fine but the engine rpm was reading zero.

Jimmy made a beautiful landing on the lake bed and shut everything down. Then we climbed out and sat in the shade of the H-43 to await "rescue." While waiting, I commented to Jimmy that I didn't see any unusual control activity after the engine rpm started to fall off. His reply was to the effect that this was the smoothest entry to autorotation that he had experienced. After what seemed hours but was probably not more 20 minutes an H-21 "Flying Banana" came out and picked us up for a vibrating return flight to Test Ops.

After maintenance reclaimed the H-43 it was determined that we had not experienced an engine failure but rather a broken tachometer cable. Jimmy hypothesized that the cable must have broken just before he "chopped" the throttle (i.e., rapidly lowered the collective), and when he saw the rpm start to drop, he smoothly lowered the collective which resulted in the "no sweat" transition to autorotation.

Later, Jimmy Honaker was demonstrating simulated engine failure to Gene Colvin, a very experienced HU-1A pilot. When they "chopped" the power, one of the rotors hit the tail assembly with the result that the H-43 suffered blade damage and had a severe nose-down pitch. Jimmy got out through his normal entry door and parachuted safely. Gene had trouble getting his door opened. Fortunately for Gene, the windscreen had broken and he was able to climb over the instrument pedestal, crawl through the remnants of the windscreen, and get his chute open. The bad news for Gene was that he had just drawn a per diem advance of several hundred dollars - which was a lot of money in those days — and he and his wallet got separated. He landed safely but never recovered his wallet or any of the advance.

(A footnote to the Honaker-Colvin incident: Jimmy carried a wire recorder on which he recorded details of the test flights. When playing back the recording after the accident, the following was heard: "Now I am lowering the collective and (bang, bang, crash, crash) GET OUT! GET OUT! ... (silence)...Now that wasn't so bad was it?" This of course brought down the house for those listening. What had happened was that Jimmy was recording over a previous flight and during the bail out, the recorder stopped. Then, after power up, the recorder continued with a prior flight which was not an autorotational entry.)

After this incident, Jimmy and I had another discussion of the adjective to use to describe the handling qualities after an engine failure. I believe that we agreed upon "extreme" for the report — and it seems to me that an "extreme" response is "excessive." Luckily for me, I never got my true introduction to an engine failure—simulated or otherwise— in an H-43.

(Thanks to John N. "Johnny" Johnson for providing the details on the Honaker-Colvin incident).

THE UCX FLIGHT TEST PROGRAM
by Charles A. Neyhart, Maj. USAF (Ret.)

In December 1956, a USAF Source Selection Board was convened to find new aircraft to fulfill the requirements in the UTX (Utility Trainer X) and UCX (Utility Cargo X) Categories. The UTX finally selected was the North American Sabreliner or T-39. The UCX selected was the Lockheed C-140. This story is about the first USAF UCX flight on 5 June 1958.

Major Reece Martin, Flight Test Operations, and I, Flight Test Engineering, were both on the Source Selection Board to look over the various aircraft company offerings in the two categories mentioned. As I recall, we visited six aircraft companies on our itinerary. In June 1958, the Lockheed version of the UCX arrived at Edwards for company flight test prior to Air Force flights. On 5 June, Maj Martin and I went over to the Lockheed flight test hangar to go over the aircraft and, if it was ready, to fly it for the Air Force. The first prototype UCX was N329J and it was a dandy. The only difference between the prototype and the production version was that the prototype had two Bristol Orpheus 1/5 engines rather than the four engines of less thrust used on production models.

After a thorough pre-flight and cockpit familiarization we started the engines and taxied out for takeoff. Everything went as smooth as silk for the first hour or so and Reece decided to do some dynamic stability testing. This was a qualitative flight only with no test instrumentation on board. On

Lockheed C-140.

the first "pull-up" at cruise speed, there was a resounding whoop followed by a very loud sound of rushing air. Reece immediately throttled back to slow the aircraft and I called for a chase plane to come and look us over and try to determine what had happened. I think it was Maj. Don Sorlie who was flying an F-86 who answered the call for help. He looked over the top and both sides of the aircraft and told us that so far everything looked OK. We still had the loud sound of rushing air so he went underneath for a look. He said "You are missing a piece of metal about four feet square from the bottom of the plane." The aircraft flew all right so we headed in to land. After an uneventful landing, the Lockheed crew was waiting with a replacement, and after securing it with the required number of DZUS fasteners, we continued our flight for a total of four hours and 55 minutes.

It seems that the problem was that Lockheed maintenance had removed the panel to inspect the hydraulic lines, etc., and replaced it with only two DZUS fasteners secured on opposite corners. They thought that we would look up inside before flight and then the panel would be properly installed. We did not look, and they did not properly secure the panel. On the first "pull up" the g-forces caused the panel to bow, the air got under it and tore it off. No other damage resulted.

AUTOROTATIONAL DESCENT
by Don Macpherson

With two years experience as a Flight Test Engineer at Lockheed, I came to work as a Flight Test Engineer at the Air Force Flight Test Center. My new boss, Keith Putnam of the Rotary Wing Section, indoctrinated me into rotary wing flight test. He told me flying in helicopters was much safer than flying in fixed wing aircraft. If anything went wrong, the pilot would lower the collective, enter autorotational descent, and make a landing almost anywhere. Keith added that the only reason to wear a parachute was because of Air Force regulations. He said there were only two circumstances where their use might be required: One was control failure and the other was fire. In the case of control failure, however, you wouldn't be able to exit the aircraft and in case of fire, you wouldn't need to because with proper use of controls, the smoke and flames could be kept away from the occupants, a landing made, and the fire put out by use of the on-board extinguishers. This would save the taxpayers a large expense. Sounded good to a young guy eager to make his mark. So with this raft of knowledge I began my tenure in rotary wing flight test.

One of the first tests Walt Hodgson and I conducted on the YH-40

Bell YH-40 "Huey" prototype.

(the prototype for the U S Army's UH-1 series of helicopters) was autorotational descents. We were to determine how the rate of descent was affected by airspeed. This was accomplished by conducting tests from 10000 feet down to around 3500 feet pressure altitude, well above the ground altitude at Edwards, at various airspeeds, and recording the resulting rate of descent. While making an autorotational descent test at the normal rotor speed of 314 rpm it happened: At an altitude of around 5000 feet the rotor speed rapidly dropped below 260 rpm.

Something was definitely wrong; even I could determine that. I remembered my boss's discussion, however we were already in autorotation. So what did the pilot do? He increased power by raising the collective. This resulted in our ability to maintain level flight with a rotor speed of approximately 290 rpm but the vibration was so severe that the instrument panel was barely readable and the horizon was a blur. Next, Walt lowered the collective to the point that the vibration was tolerable which resulted in a rotor speed of around 260 rpm. Now things weren't going according to my boss's instructions. So I decided that use of the "required" parachute might be in order. I looked over the side and saw the ground about 2500 feet below, an awfully long way down. Besides, if I got out, the aircraft center of gravity would move aft and we were already at an aft cg. This would not be fair to the other occupants. My next decision was that maybe my boss's statements weren't so bad. We were almost in autorotation, the helicopter did not appear to be falling apart, at least not at the moment, and there was a chance we soon would be on the ground in one piece.

During our descent, Walt radioed that we were making a landing on the southern part of Rogers Dry Lake. The tower asked if it was an emergency. Walt said "stand by." As we approached the ground a flare was made and we touched down at a rate of descent of approximately 700 feet per minute. The aircraft bounced four times and skidded to a stop 110 yards from the touchdown point. I was feeling relieved at being "safely" on the ground but as I started to relax Walt slowly raised the collective with no immediate result. Suddenly the helicopter jumped approximately one foot in the air starting to vibrate again. Walt slowly lowered the collective and the aircraft abruptly descended one foot and contacted the ground. At that point I suggested he shut the sucker down before anything else happened. The control tower in the meantime was calling, wanting to know if we were going to declare an emergency. Walt finally told them we would need some kind of transportation. At that point the whole base seemed to light up. Fire trucks, an ambulance, staff cars, and a rescue helicopter rushed toward us all abreast, each trying to be the first to arrive. The ensuing dust cloud obliterated the main base. My thoughts raced: "I hope they don't run right over us." We were picked up and taken back for interrogation.

Upon inspecting the helicopter, the maintenance folks discovered a failure in the main rotor collective pitch control bearing in the scissors and sleeve assembly (a 100 hour part with only 99 hours and 55 minutes on it). Consequently no collective pitch control was possible and the rotor blades, free to pitch at will, were restrained only by cyclic control links and the stabilizer bar. LOSS OF CONTROL. I remembered Keith Putnam saying something about not being able to exit the aircraft. I felt like taking a piece of a damaged aircraft back to him, throwing it on his desk, and saying I quit. Fortunately I was able to control my feelings.

TOUCHDOWN!
by John N. Johnson

Although the H-13H was an Army (MASH) helicopter, the Air Force was conducting engineering tests for the Army during this time frame. A portion of the flight test program for the H-13H was to establish a height-velocity curve (better known as the deadman's curve). It is the combination of height above the ground and airspeed from which a safe autorotational landing could be made in the event of an engine failure.

The H-13 incorporated a skid type landing gear, and as a result,

Bell H-13H.

during a running touchdown the nose would tend to pitch down and the tail up. At this point the normal instinct is to apply aft cyclic. As a result, numerous tails had been chopped off in operational use. Captain Robert G. Ferry and myself were determined that this would not happen to us, so we decided to relocate the ground handling wheels to the forward section of the skids so that when the tail pitched up and the nose down, the wheels would contact the ground causing the skids to level with the ground. Now that Bob and I solved that problem we needed a location to conduct the tests. We didn't want to use the runway or dry lake because of wearing out the skids in only a few landings (no spares). So we started looking for a nice grassy area. Where in 1958 at Edwards Air Force Base could a person find a grassy field? You're right! The High School football field. Well, we proceeded to the Base Commander who (after much persuasion) gave his permission if it was all right with the school principal. After explaining the situation to the principal, he readily agreed. However, we could not remove the goal posts.

After walking and flying around the field, Bob felt that we could conduct the tests with no problems. Prior to obtaining quantitative data, we established a conservative qualitative curve, using a barometric altimeter. Our procedure was to establish a combination of height above the ground and airspeed, chop the throttle, hold controls fixed for two seconds, then initiate recovery. The two seconds was estimated to be the time required in an operational situation to recognize an engine failure.

The test method was to hold airspeed constant for a series of test points and decrease the height after each test point. As we approached each end point, we would decrease height approximately 25 feet. As we were approaching one end point, I suddenly forgot how to subtract. Twenty-five feet became 50 feet which caused us to initiate what we thought to be an end point 25 feet lower than intended. Well, it was an end point (plus 25 feet). Fortunately Bob very cleverly maneuvered the helicopter to the ground without incident, although we touched down faster and harder than planned. This caused the nose to pitch down. The ground handling wheels took over and brought the tail down without aft cyclic and everything worked beautifully. About the time we started to relax and were slowing down, we looked forward and saw the goal posts rapidly approaching. With a rotor diameter of 35 feet and goal post spread of 34 feet, Bob was going to have to exercise some extremely precise flying skills. Fortunately, we stopped just prior to the goal posts and recorded another data point.

HELICOPTER HIGH ELEVATION TEST SITE
by John N. Johnson

We were getting ready to conduct high altitude take-off and landing tests on the H-13H Bell helicopter at Coyote Flats (an elevation of 9800 feet). The H-21 tandem-rotor helicopter was being used to ferry support equipment and personnel into Coyote Flats with Major Bill Ballantine, who had recently been checked out by Captain Bob Ferry, at the controls and with Army Captain John L. Johns, Liason Officer, flying as co-pilot. There were five personnel plus equipment to survey the area for positioning the Fairchild Flight Analyzers for recording H-13H take-off and landing data. Keith Putnam was kneeling between the two pilots while the H-21 was circling and gaining altitude to clear the ridge into Coyote Flats. Suddenly, Keith came running back shouting "We're going to hit...Tighten your belts." About the time he got strapped in, we hit with a good jolt. Fortunately, we landed in the only clear area, although the left-side of the rotors were clipping the tree limbs and the right was over a 300-foot ravine. It was clear straight ahead, so we off-loaded the helicopter of three people and 1500 pounds of equipment. The flight crew was able to taxi about 200 yards to the ridge and then take-off because they were much lighter. Of course, they said they would be right back!

The original plan was to meet with two G.I. trucks with additional equipment and supplies. Well, the helicopter had cooking utensils, no food, personal hunting and plinking weapons, no ammunition, and one sleeping bag. Nothing was complete—lesson learned. As we reached the ridge where

Piasecki H-21 at high altitude test site.

the H-21 took off, we could see the trucks. "We're saved!" but no — they were instructed to return to Bishop if we had not arrived by 1300 hours.

It was now 1400 hours and they were on their way back to Bishop, a 2 to 2 1/2 hour drive (about 15 miles). No problem, we'll wave at them and they will see us and come back...not from two miles. What now, coach? Well, we knew there was a cabin used by Sierra mountain hikers about three miles away, so away we went. Fortunately, we all had good hiking boots as it was not your usual walk around the block after dinner.

We arrived at the cabin three hours later with one sleeping bag. There was nothing in sight except a small single engine fixed wing aircraft coming down the valley. He made one pass, circled, then threw down a roll of toilet paper and left. As it was floating down, Keith says, "Here we are tired, hungry...it's getting late and cold... and they throw us a roll of toilet paper." I suggested to Keith that maybe there was a note on the paper, and sure enough there was. (Keith was on his way to becoming a brilliant engineer and was also very practical. However, that one went completely over his head.) The note stated that the helicopter was broken — on landing the empennage failed internally. However, the trucks were located and diverted back to the cabin with food, sleeping bags, and, I'm sure, more toilet paper.

Everything was downhill from that point except while I went to retrieve the equipment we off loaded from the helicopter, everyone had snacks and cookies around my sleeping bag...and all that night the rats kept waking me up.

AND THEN THE FINANCE OFFICER SAID ...
by John N. Johnson

Helicopters have different hovering capabilities at different weights and altitudes — and the hovering capabilities are different depending on whether
you are in or out of ground effect. Early on, Keith Putnam adapted some data
analysis techniques to provide a non-dimensional presentation that is analo-
gous to the lift coefficient versus drag coefficient presentations for fixed wings.
Unfortunately, we all got carried away with this non-dimensional approach
and started presenting curves in the report for weights and altitudes that were
not actually demonstrated.

Paul Bikle "explained" to Keith and Fred Stoliker that flight testers
don't present data in flight test reports unless the test conditions were within
10 percent of the data presented — regardless of the extrapolations from the
non-dimensional curves. While their scars were healing, we set out to find
different locations where we could attempt to define the in-ground-effect
hovering capabilities.

Suitable locations were found at Bakersfield — essentially sea level;
Edwards — 2300 feet; Bishop — approximately 4100 feet; Long Valley —
approximately 7100 feet; and Coyote Flats — about 9800 feet in the Sierra
mountains. All of the locations except Coyote Flats had suitable lodging and
messing facilities nearby and some limited aviation services. However, Coyote

"Government furnished accommodations" at high altitude test site.

Flats was a dirt strip that had nothing but dirt — everything had to be trucked or flown in and out. Most of the time the crews stayed in Bishop but occasionally, the flight and ground crews stayed overnight at the flats using tents to ensure an early start on tests.

The "Desert Wings" (local base newspaper) got wind of the testing at Coyote Flats and sent a reporter and photographer to interview the test team. The test crew gave them a great story of how they suffered many privations high in the mountains living in tents and eating rations. When the story was published, the test crews were in their glory until the Finance Officer called. He noted that since the crews were living in government-furnished quarters (tents) and eating government-furnished meals (rations), they should not have collected per diem. He asked that all per diem for tests at Coyote Flats be returned immediately.

Actually, the only rations provided were limited amounts of chocolate bars and unlimited quantities of water purification pills. After several session with the Finance Officer and additional photos, we convinced him that the tents were used to protect the valuable, sensitive data recording equipment and not for personnel. We also advised him that we provided our own rations, which we really did.

FIRST MATING OF THE X-15 TO THE NB-52
by Bob Hoey

In 1958, after completing a couple of stability and control projects (F-100C and F-104A) I was lucky enough to be assigned to the AF/NASA X-15 flight test team. Jack Wesesky was my boss and Dick Harer was the AFFTC Project Officer. Capt. Iven Kincheloe was the assigned AF test pilot.

Besides the famous X-1, the X-15 is probably the best known of all of the rocket-powered research aircraft. Its mission was to expand the realm of manned, controlled flight from about Mach 3 and 126,000 ft. altitude (touched briefly by the ill-fated X-2) to above Mach 6 and over 250,000 feet altitude. Surface skin temperatures of over 1200 degrees F were expected over much of the airplane. The thermal environment would push the state of the art in metallurgy and fabrication as well as the glass panes for the cockpit. There were serious questions as to how to lubricate and feed propellants to subsystems which were to operate for over two minutes at zero g. The g environment for the pilot was also quite severe. In addition to the two minutes at zero g, the pilot would experience an axial acceleration of over four g during boost, and six g through the seat of the pants simultaneously with a three g axial deceleration during entry.

North American X-15 mated to NB-52 Mothership.

Interestingly, the configuration of the airplane was a relatively minor challenge. NACA and North American Aviation (NAA) had selected a configuration which was a straight-forward Mach 2 design (notice the similarity to the F-104) that could be pushed to Mach-6-plus with pure brute force. There was very little finesse in the aerodynamic design process. The landing gear skids were mounted externally along the aft fuselage. The ten-degree wedge airfoil of the vertical tail provided high directional stability at high Mach number, but added significantly to the drag at low speed. But low speed flight and landings were known quantities that could be addressed head-on. High speed directional stability was an unknown, thus the conservative approach was chosen.

The boost phase would last a mere 80 seconds, during which the airplane would accelerate from subsonic conditions at 45,000 ft. to more than 6 times the speed of sound at over 100,000 ft. altitude when the fuel was depleted. It was more like being shot out of a cannon than flying an airplane. The piloting task to achieve the desired trajectory during boost was obviously a major challenge, as was the final, "dead-stick" landing with abnormally high drag. My initial task was to work on some simulator studies to develop the best landing technique for the airplane — it would be a glider with a max L/D of about 4.25.

When the first X-15 was delivered to Edwards the excitement began to build. The airplane was still in North American's possession, so us government types were just spectators. We had heard that the #1 airplane was to be mated to the wing pylon on the NB-52 mothership for the first time early one morning.

Dick Harer and I drove down the flight line and across the ramp just as the sun was coming up. It was truly an awesome sight - this huge silver mothership glinting in the sun with this little, all-black rocket ship tucked under one wing! Seven or eight NAA technicians, dressed in white coveralls, were standing around this marvel of new technology. As we got closer we could see that there was still a gap of about one foot between the pylon and the X-15. We got out of the car and walked toward the airplanes. One technician was lying on his stomach on the top of the X-15 with his hands in the area between the two vehicles. We could hear the unmistakable sound of a hack saw as he cut away a piece of interfering structure.

So much for "high tech"! Obviously the "bigger hammer" rule was now in effect.

LOW L/D LANDING APPROACHES
by Jack Wesesky

In 1958, North American Aviation (NAA) was developing the X-15 research airplane and was contracted to prove its airworthiness up to Mach 3. The NACA (later designated NASA) and the AFFTC were to conduct the research program, including the envelope expansion to the design limit under the technical direction of NACA. Captain Iven Kincheloe was the designated Air Force pilot and Robert G. (Bob) Hoey was an AFFTC flight test engineer assigned to the Manned Spacecraft Engineering Office to participate in the X-15 program. At the time I was the chief of that office. Capt. Kincheloe and Bob were exploring the lift/drag characteristics of a number of F-104 configurations to try to match the predicted X-15 lift/drag characteristics in the gliding approach and landing phase. The large base area of the X-15 engine and wedge tail gave a subsonic maximum L/D of only 4.25, considerably below the L/D of previous rocket powered research airplanes.

Bob was also exploring the expected X-15 performance in the landing phase using the AFFTC GEDA (Goodyear Electronic Data Analyzer) analog computer tied in to voltmeters, ammeters and a B-17 bombardier's stick (two axes) bolted to a wooden chair as a crude simulator. Bob found that, using NAA's recommended approach speed (240 knots - maximum L/D), he could not touch down with less than 5 feet per second sink rate. This was the design limit for the X-15. The normal question to ask was how valid was the simulator mechanization. So Bob cranked in the F-104 characteristics in place of the X-15 and found no problem with greasing the F-104 touchdown with the configurations selected to duplicate the X-15 L/D. Captain Kincheloe also flew the X-15 and F-104 simulations with similar results.

Bob noted that the moments of inertia about the wing axis (Iyy) of the X-15 at landing were greater than that of the F-104. This was undoubtedly due to the mass of the instrumentation and the electronics equipment in the nose and the engine in the tail of the X-15 with large empty fuel cells in the fuselage as compared to the engine in the fuselage of the F-104. He also theorized that (in spite of the large slab tail) the elevator effectiveness of the X-15 at the low speed associated with completion of the flare, was not sufficient for precise pitch control of the aircraft. This resulted in leveling off above the ground, then descending at a high rate of sink at touchdown.

Bob tried using higher approach speeds to complete the flare at higher speeds for more precise control leading to touchdown. Although this had a more rapid rate of descent during approach, he noted that there was sufficient lift and pitch control to arrest the rate of descent during the flare. Speed at completion of flare had good control effectiveness to fly a very shallow glide slope while decelerating to touchdown. This resulted in a one foot per second sink rate at touchdown.

Joe Walker and Neil Armstrong, research pilots for NACA, were also experimenting with low L/D approaches using an F-104 under the engineering guidance of Gene Matranga. They made successful landings with maximum L/D's as low as 2.7. They had independently found that a higher approach speed gave better control of touchdown conditions. It was during these tests that someone asked Joe Walker about accuracy of the touchdown point relative to landing on a 10,000 foot runway. Joe's classic response was, "There's no question WHERE you're going to land, it's HOW HARD!"

The first three X-15 flights, flown by the NAA pilot, used approach speeds of 240 knots. Each resulted in a rate of sink of about 5 feet per second at touchdown. Then on the fourth flight, a minor explosion in one of the XLR-11 rocket engines required an engine shut-down and jettisoning of the propellants for an emergency landing on Rosamond Dry Lake. Because of the steep nose down attitude of the airplane during descent, all propellants could not be jettisoned and the X-15 landed at an abnormally heavy weight, again with a five feet per second rate of sink at touchdown. The fuselage broke.

NAA agreed to try the higher speed approach for the next X-15 flight; this resulted in a rate of sink at touchdown of only about one foot per second. All subsequent X-15 landings used approach speeds of 300 knots or greater with acceptable rates of sink at touchdown.

This landing approach method became standard for all unpowered low L/D aircraft such as the Lifting Bodies and the Space Shuttle.

§

The "Space Race" had shifted into high gear. NASA had initiated the Mercury capsule program to place a man in space as soon as possible and selected the first seven Astronauts.

The North American X-15 made its initial glide and powered flights piloted by Scott Crossfield. A new altitude record was established by the F-104A as Capt. Joe Jordan performed a zoom to 103,395 feet.

The old NACA High Speed Flight Station became the NASA Flight Research Center. Project "High Range", consisting of a 400-mile string of radars and data acquisition sites, data recording and transmission, and communications equipment to support the X-15 program, became operational.

Nine AFFTC radars were operational to support flight tests. NASA-Flight Research Center (FRC) established an aerodynamics test range.

B-58A FLIGHT — THRILLS AT 23 MILES A MINUTE
by Rob Ransone Copyright (c) 1995 Ransone Associates, Inc.
Used by permission

The B-58A "Hustler", manufactured by General Dynamics (GD-Fort Worth), was the world's first Mach 2 bomber and first flew in November 1956. With a sleek, area-ruled fuselage, four mighty GE J-79 afterburning engines slung under a rakish, 60-degree swept delta wing, it was probably one of the most beautiful airplanes ever built. The airplane, called the "return component," because that is all that would come back from a bombing mission, carried a large pod, containing one nuclear bomb and extra fuel, slung under the fuselage centerline. With a maximum takeoff weight of 163,000 pounds, one forgot that it was only 20% larger (in every dimension) than the Convair F-102 from which it got its shape. More fighter than bomber, there was only one pilot — no copilot — with a control stick rather than a yoke, and we all had separate, tandem cockpits.

The B-58A was ahead of its time. It ventured too far "toward the unknown" in many respects, and had twice the accident rate of the notorious F-104A Starfighter. During the year that we did the Category II performance tests out of GD's plant next to Carswell AFB in Fort Worth, Texas, of the 30 airplanes flying, six were lost along with half of their crews. I was never afraid when we were actually in the air, because we were busy, either with our flight test work, or with trying to solve some problem and get back on the ground in one piece. I will confess to a few butterflies immediately before some flights, however, especially after our test pilot quit. "There are too many things going on in that airplane that I don't know about — I can't even see the wings!" This was immediately after one airplane ran off the end of the runway and exploded, and another just blew up on the ramp during preflight. Then Charlie Bock became our test pilot. Good move. A superb test pilot.

Hey, Rob. Got any extra fuel in your flight station?

In-flight refueling was a major element in our performance flight tests, because the B-58A was so difficult to maintain and we got so few flights a month. Once we got in the air, we hated to come down. SAC was very cooperative, and supported us out of Carswell AFB. Unfortunately, the B-58A's fuel gauges were not accurate enough to determine our test weights. I studied a plan of the fuel lines, and determined that two fuel flow meters, strategically placed, would allow us to meter the fuel as we received it from the tanker. The only catch was that we did not know how much fuel went into the pod tanks until we transferred it all up into the airplane itself. No problem — we established a routine of emptying the pod tanks into the airplane before landing.

Except on one flight, after which, when I was studying the post flight fuel counter data, I noticed that 5000 pounds of fuel had left the pod, but

General Dynamics' YB-58A "Hustler" in composite configuration.

never arrived in the airplane. After marveling at this for a few minutes, I called the crew chief. "I'm missing 5000 pounds of JP-4 that disappeared between the pod and the airplane."

"No it didn't — I just found it," he replied. "It's sloshing around in the belly of the airplane!"

"...and wash our windshield, please" at 25,000 feet

Our supersonic flights out of Fort Worth were limited in 1959. We would fly north to Liberal, Kansas, turn south, and accelerate to Mach 2. We had only a few minutes of test time before we had to turn north again at the Gulf of Mexico (we were not cleared to fly over water). To give us more supersonic flight test time, I developed a plan to fly to Edwards, conducting subsonic performance tests on the way, refuel from a SAC KC-135 tanker over Edwards, then fly supersonic back to Fort Worth. If we had a problem refueling, we could land at Edwards because another B-58 was being tested there, and there was ground support.

All went well until we tried to refuel over Edwards at 25,000 feet. The refueling receptacle was in the nose, directly in front of the pilot. When Charlie Bock engaged the toggles to clamp down on the KC-135's refueling probe, a white fog suddenly erupted from the receptacle, and in less than a minute, all four forward windshield panels were coated with hydraulic fluid. The tanker was visible only through the upper canopy windows. Charlie disconnected from the tanker and closed the refuel receptacle. With no windshield wipers (on a Mach 2 airplane? Get real!) we didn't know how long it would take for the wind blast to clear the windshield. Supersonic airflow might do it, but if anyone wanted to go supersonic with a known hydraulic leak, he wasn't on OUR airplane! Charlie expressed concern about whether he could even see well enough to land.

After some thought, I suggested that the tanker might wash our windshield with a cupful of JP-4. Charlie said that he had also been thinking about that, so he asked the tanker. Carl Simmons, another Edwards flight test engineer on the program, was on the tanker, and he said the tanker crew was stunned. "What if we get fuel into the engine inlets — we'll all blow up!" Carl told them that the guys back in the B-58 hadn't just fallen off a turnip truck. "If they didn't think it safe, they wouldn't have asked." The tanker pilot finally agreed, and the boom operator talked Charlie back under the boom, and, with one small squirt, cleaned our windshield slick as a whistle! We then landed at Edwards, where I lived for two days in my flight suit.

From Edwards, we did a maximum performance takeoff and accelerated immediately to Mach 2 towards Fort Worth. We passed Albuquerque, started decelerating over west Texas, and arrived over Fort Worth only 45

YB-58 Heavy Weight Performance test crew. L to r: Capt. E. Bradley, (unknown S/Sgt.), 1st Lt. "Rob" Ransone.

minutes after brake release at Edwards. We got all of our Mach 1.6, 1.8, and 2.0 cruise performance done in one stretch. We landed at Fort Worth just as another B-58 was taking off. Moments later it disintegrated over southern Oklahoma during a Mach 2 engine shutdown at 36,000 feet, killing its two-man crew.

So why did three pros almost jump out of a perfectly good airplane?

Other amusing fuel things happened in the B-58A that entertained us on our long "boring" flights. For example, on one flight, as we were returning to base, Charlie Bock mentioned over the intercom that he had just lost the aft fuel booster pumps. The fuse panel was in my flight test engineer's station, so I announced that I would check. Sure enough, the aft booster pump fuse was blown. I looked around for a spare. "Charlie, I think I've found a spare the right size. There was something written next to it that has been erased. I think it's a spare. I'll pull it, and if anything happens, you holler." Charlie said "OK."

I pulled the fuse. Immediately there was loud, excited hollering in our earphones. Then silence. The crew chief, in the second crew station asked, tentatively: "Uh...that wasn't you, was it Charlie?" Charlie said "No. It scared the hell out of me!" The fuse had blown again. We landed without further incident, but we never found out who had keyed his mike and yelled at that exact moment.

A little bit of data from a lot of airplanes

Not all of the thrills of flight test come in the air. Sometimes they come from some clever discovery during data analysis. Non-flight test engineers won't believe this — just take my word for it. For example, to determine the altitude at which to top out our Mach 2 check climb plots, I had to know the altitude at which the B-58A started its cruise climb mode.

We had determined that the best Mach 2 range was at maximum afterburner power, letting the airplane climb as it burned fuel. Don't scoff — fuel was galloping through the four engines at 60,000 pounds per hour! So I needed the Mach 2 cruise performance data in order to finish my climb to ceiling plots. This was going to take a while for the other engineer to complete, because of the complex calculations needed to correct the data to standard conditions. Furthermore, these corrections depended upon analysis of our own flight test data, that would not be ready for several months.

In order to expedite matters, I collected all of the data I could find from other B-58As flying at Mach 2 at maximum power and cruise climb. All I really needed was their gross weights, altitudes, and the ambient air temperature. I collected data snippets from about a dozen flights, and plotted them as altitude versus temperature for lines of constant w/delta. The lines for individual airplanes showed much steeper slopes and variations than the aggregate trend. This was before the days of powerful little computers that come in cereal boxes, so I had to draw slopes and temperature corrections by hand. (Yes, I could have done it on the latest IBM 704 computer, for which a programmer would have written a long program — in "octal" — and I would still be waiting for the answers).

Guess what? the data came out fine. My cruise ceilings were within 500 feet of the "properly" corrected cruise climb data that we got out of the computers six months later. What fun!

"You had your hand on the stick!" "No I didn't!" "Yes you did!"

As a result of the accident over Oklahoma, several changes were made in the B-58A's flight control system. The initial structural failure to that airplane, caused when it exceeded the 1.75-degree sideslip limit for Mach 2 at 36,000 feet, was that the aft fuselage was literally twisted off from the side loads on the vertical tail. It was like someone had grabbed a child's airplane and twisted off its tail. Less than two degrees sideslip doesn't sound like much, but, believe me, at Mach 2, where the dynamic pressure was over 1000 pounds per square foot, the side forces had us literally hanging against our shoulder harnesses.

For this next story, you engineers need to know a little more about the B-58A's flight control system. To counter an outboard engine failure at Mach 2, where Cnb (directional stability) is getting pretty low anyway, a very large vertical fin and rudder were provided. Because of its height above the airplane's center of gravity, large rudder deflections caused a considerable rolling moment, which was automatically counteracted by opposite aileron through a mechanical linkage. But these weren't normal ailerons, they were "elevons" that, on the delta wing planform, provided elevator functions collectively, and aileron functions differentially. With a positive static margin (this was before microcomputers could make barn doors stable) some up elevon was needed for longitudinal stability. Aileron movements resulted in more deflection on one side and less on the other side, which caused differential drag, which resulted in yaw due to aileron, which required rudder deflections to counter, which...anyway, you get my drift. All of this was handled automatically through a mechanical aileron rudder interconnect (ARI). In addition, the airplane had rate dampers for roll, pitch, and yaw.

The ARI ratios were changed, as a result of the Oklahoma accident, and these changes had to be reevaluated. Also, the airplane was placarded to prohibit supersonic flight with dampers inoperative. Fine. Don't go supersonic without your dampers on, but what if they fail at Mach 2? How do you get down? Re-enter the steely, blue-eyed team from Edwards. This time, the pilot was Fitz Fulton, another truly great test pilot. Once again we were flying out of GD in Fort Worth. (The fact that my mother lived in Fort Worth had nothing to do with all of this TDY!) Our mission, in September of 1960, was to evaluate the effects of the new ARI ratios on handling qualities, and to see if the airplane could be decelerated from Mach 2 with all dampers off.

With dampers on, all pulses were essentially deadbeat. Good. That's what dampers are supposed to do. Dampers off, however, was more sporting. With the yaw damper off and the roll and pitch dampers on, at Mach 1.2, lateral-directional damping took 9 cycles and 24 seconds to half-amplitude. The roll damper inputs were driving the oscillations through the ARI. At Mach 2, with roll and yaw dampers off, the oscillations started going divergent in two or three cycles. Bad news. But on analyzing the oscillograph records — back in those days, we had to read the oscillograph records by candle light — I noticed that the lateral stick movements, although very small, were leading the airplane oscillations. I asked Fitz why he didn't let go of the stick.

"I did let go."

"No, you didn't!"

"Yes I did, but... I kept my hand around it so that I could grab it quickly."

"Your body motions, driven by the airplane movement, are bumping your hand against the stick enough to drive the oscillations."

The next time, he held his hand farther away from the stick, and, sure enough, the airplane motions slowly damped out. Very slowly. At supersonic Mach numbers, the oscillations were very easily excited and very lightly damped, and manual attempts to control them could easily lead to in-phase coupling and loss of the plane and crew. In trying to fly the airplane with the roll and pitch dampers off, Fitz had to turn the dampers on quickly, on several attempts, in order to recover the aircraft from its divergent lateral-directional oscillations. Very quickly! (Remember the 1.75-degree sideslip limit, and Oklahoma, where the wind blows 1400 miles an hour across the plain.)

The lateral-directional motions exhibited large roll and small yaw excursions, which suggested using the ailerons to damp the oscillations. Bad choice. The yaw due to aileron drove the divergence. Fitz found that he could damp the oscillations if he ignored the large roll oscillations and concentrated on controlling the small yaw motion with the rudder pedals. It worked. No yaw, then no Dutch roll. But Fitz found a better method — just put in a small amount of sideslip, which had a strong damping effect. That is the method that was added to the flight manual. Fitz also found that, with practice and concentration, he could control the Dutch roll with aileron, but that method was too tricky for mere mortal pilots. The oscillograph records substantiated what we had found.

Our big test came at Mach 2, when Fitz turned all dampers off, flew straight and level for a few seconds, and then reduced power to idle for a deceleration to subsonic speed. I'm here to tell you that it worked fine.

CONVAIR 880 OUT OF CONTROL
by Johnny Armstrong

They were new — these jet transports and the Air Force was conducting a short evaluation of each; the Boeing 707, the Douglas DC-8, and the Convair 880. All of us flight test engineers were aching to get a chance to go for a ride. By now I was a seasoned multi-jet airplane rider. I had recently completed serving as flight test engineer assistant to Everett Dunlap on the first Air Force evaluation of the B-58 at Fort Worth. My opportunity to ride one of these future replacements of the DC-7s and Constellation prop airliners came when Lt. Charlie Crawford was assigned the lead engineer for the 880 evaluation.......I should have known better! (Last time I rode with Charlie on one of his projects I ended up taking a bath in the Pacific Ocean.....re: the Ruptured Duck SA-16B story.)

This was the number three Convair 880 and it was set up in typical flight test fashion with only a few airline type seats, photopanel station, and water ballast tanks. It also had a bail out tunnel located aft of the cockpit on the right side of the aircraft. During preflight walkaround we were shown the actuator handle which, when rotated, would actuate the extension of the tunnel downward below the exterior of the fuselage into the airstream to hopefully allow a freefall clear of the aircraft without recontact.

What a smooth ride that day, 16 April 1959, flying at 35,000 feet over the Antelope Valley except for the intentional upsets by the rudder kicks, aileron rolls and other test maneuvers. The cockpit crew for the flight was a Convair pilot in the left seat, an Air Force Flight Test Center pilot in the co-pilot's seat and an FAA pilot in the jump seat. I was sitting in the aft part of the fuselage and Charlie was seated at the photopanel station located mid fuselage near the center of gravity.

Another test maneuver input and the aircraft responded with an oscillation....and then all hell broke loose. I seem to remember now 36 years later that the first terror was the noise and high frequency vibration followed instantaneously by the unfamiliar low frequency motions and g forces. The vibrations seemed severe enough that my mind concluded that the aircraft structure could fail and we were totally out of control in an unrecoverable situation. I write this years later like I was analyzing all this at the time. What was really going on was total terror and the thought that I was going to die. Natural survival instincts took over and I started to head toward the bail out tunnel. I already had my back pack chute on so I unbuckled the lap seat belt and got out of my seat only to find myself thrown to the floor of the aircraft due to the g forces. So I continued to crawl on my hands and knees toward the front of the aircraft. Looking to my left I saw Crawford still seated at his photopanel station with a very strange expression on his face which at the time I categorized as a look of death. The g force remained positive as I continued up the open spaces of the stripped fuselage interior. I next observed that the FAA pilot had exited the cockpit and was going through strange looking contortions trying to put on a backpack parachute with his body bending in strange shapes as it was being pulled down by the g force. At that time I knew I would have company diving through the bailout tunnel. I was getting closer to my life saving escape hatch when all of a sudden the vibration, noise, and three axis motions ceased. All I recall now is next I was back in my seat all buckled in and still scared that it could happen again. Soon Capt. Joe Jordan in an F-100 was in formation with us assuring us we seemed to have all the important parts of the aircraft still attached that would allow us to return to Edwards. It was reassuring seeing that F-100 chase aircraft off our wing and hearing Joe's familiar voice as we were heading home. Even so, each time the 880 dropped its wing for a heading change I felt uncomfortable. Finally...the secure feeling of the jar of touchdown and the shriek of the tires leaving rubber on the Edwards runway...we made it!

The 880 had gone through two 360-degree rolls at critical Mach number resulting in the loss of 10,000 feet. A cam in the mechanical flight control system stuck and resulted in a wing spoiler becoming stuck in the deflected position until it broke loose due to the high vibration being experienced by the airframe. The good news was that the flight control system was modified and a load of paying airline customers never had to experience that E-ride. That's the ..."why" of flight test.

So, did I see my life pass in front of me as they say when the brain senses that death is near? No! I recall even to this day that as I was crawling toward the escape hatch that my mind focused on thoughts of things that were not complete or remained to be accomplished. I had just recently married a lovely blond Texas girl while on the B-58 program in Fort Worth and my thoughts were on the fact that I had not yet changed my life insurance policy from my folks to her. I was uneasy about flying again but one month later I was airborne in an experimental McDonnell aircraft Model 119M that looked like a miniature DC-8 that was in competition with the Lockheed Jetstar in the UCX program.

POP GOES THE INDICATOR
by Forrest Worthington

It was 1959 and I had been the Project Engineer for Pacer Aircraft at AFFTC for about a year when I became involved with a problem on the F-100 Pacer,

North American F-100C configured as a pacer.

Serial Number 41744. A routine airspeed cross-check had been made and the primary and secondary airspeed systems had failed to cross-check.

Airspeed cross-checks involved stabilizing at three separate airspeeds and comparing the readings of the individual systems. We always made the airspeed checks at the same three airspeeds and had developed a delta value for each system and speed.

After removing and replacing all indicators in the photo panel and cockpit, we had the integrity of all systems checked on the ground. The grounds checks were all completed satisfactorily, however the Instrument Lab where the indicators were calibrated and repaired reported that the bellows of the indicators we sent them had been over-stressed.

With the replacement indicators installed, I requested Flight Operations to accomplish another airspeed cross-check. When I received the data from this second cross-check and made the analysis, once again the F-100 had failed to pass. This time when we removed and replaced all the indicators we kept track of what system each indicator was from and found that only the wing boom indicators had been over stressed.

It was rather clear that the next action should be to find out what the preflight procedures were. I went out to the flight line and found the crew chief for the F-100 and asked him to review his preflight procedure with me. During his review he told me about the removal of the protective covers from the wing booms. These protective covers were made out of hose tubing and had duct tape covering one end. It seems that the ground crew enjoyed trying to generate a popping suction sound whenever they removed wing boom covers. I cannot remember my exact words to him but I explained what they were doing to the airspeed indicators every time they created that popping sound.

WORLD'S FIRST TURBINE POWERED HELICOPTER RESCUE
by John N. Johnson

In the spring of 1959, Major Walt Hodgson and myself had just finished the day's take-off and landing tests of the Bell Helicopter YH-40 (UH-1 series) at the Long Valley airstrip, our 7000-foot test site near Mammoth Lakes, CA. We were preparing for the next morning's flight when we were approached by two sheriffs asking if we could rescue an injured mountain climber who had fallen and was being carried to Iceberg Lake. We told them we would be happy to if we had adequate performance and if they would go through appropriate Air Force channels for authorization. We told them where to start and we would stay in the area waiting word from our channels. Amazingly enough, we received authorization within a couple of hours. Since this was a new aircraft and there was no performance data such as hovering performance, fuel consumption, etc. available, we kind of guessed how much fuel to take on to make the rescue, fly the patient to Bishop, California, and return to Long Valley. If worse came to worse, we could always land at Long Valley and refuel as we had our AF tanker trucks there.

Being concerned about gross weight we elected not to take a 16mm movie camera with us. We hooked up with a Civil Air Patrol (CAP) airplane and they were going to lead us to the rescue site although they had not been there themselves. This was great since we were not familiar with the area and there were no maps available. Well, within 15 minutes we lost contact with the CAP and were on our own. Pretty soon we spotted someone waving at us near a cleared area so Walt proceeded to make a landing. I got out and ran over to the person about 60 yards away (Ever try running 60 yards at 10,000 feet when you are not used to it and smoke? Well, don't.) When I reached the person it was a teenaged girl just waving at us. However, she did know of the accident and was able to point us in the right direction. As we approached the area we could see that Iceberg Lake was in a volcano surrounded by about 90% of the top ridge of the mountain.

As we circled the area to determine the best way in and out we saw that the lake was about 50% frozen and observed the tracks in the snow around the lake where the rescue party had carried the injured climber who had fallen

Bell YH-40 at high elevation test site.

about 300 feet. The lake was the blue-green color of iceberg water and the setting was absolutely beautiful. We determined there was only one way in and one way out. Because of the terrain we had to land into the volcano and take off going into it.

Being well prepared Boy Scouts we took a roll of toilet paper with us to throw out to determine wind direction. I threw the toilet paper out the window and it worked perfectly except it was absolutely calm. We were hoping for a little wind but it was not to be this day. In addition it was warm and we had a density altitude of about 13,000 feet. Walt made a beautiful landing. I got out of the helicopter to talk to the rescue party and doctor and show them where to position the injured man who was in a Stokes litter. I estimated his weight to be approximately 250 pounds with clothing, blankets, etc. The doctor naturally wanted to go with the patient to continue care until he could be hospitalized and also eliminate the one day mule ride back to civilization. The doctor was a large man and with all his gear I estimated 300 pounds - so now we had 550 pounds. Walt and I discussed the situation and based upon our testing at the 7000-foot site we figured if we could hover 3-5 feet we would be able to clear the obstacles in front of us, pick up airspeed while descending to near the lake, then circle and turn around within the volcano as we knew we couldn't clear it straight ahead, and had to turn around and exit the way we came in. We decided if we could not hover at that height then I would get out and he would try again. This meant that I would either have to hike out (one full day down hill) or he would have to return for me; however, a storm was approaching and with the time required to make it to the hospital, Long Valley to refuel, etc., it was doubtful he could make it back. Fortunately we could hover at approximately 4 feet and I didn't have to walk out. Walt initiated a jump take-off, cleared the obstacles, descended to the lake (approximately 100 feet) building up airspeed, turning to the right to the edge of the crater, then left circling around to our initial take-off point. We were at an approximately 50-degree bank angle and the rotor blades were close enough to the crater to be in ground effect. The remaining flight to the Bishop, California, hospital was routine, although hospital employees and visitors had to clear the parking lot as there was no landing pad. This was the successful conclusion of the world's first turbine powered helicopter rescue operation and also the first helicopter landing at the Bishop hospital. Returning to the Long Valley test strip we again started preparations for the next day's testing.

KAMAN H-43B "HUSKIE" PHASE II PRELIMINARY EVALUATION
by John N. Johnson

Early in the 1959 test program, Captain Walt Hodgson and I were returning from the first flight of the day. Taxiing to our parking area faster than normal, Walt applied brakes, but to no avail. He pulled aft cyclic to assist in slowing down. Suddenly we noticed people running behind hangar doors, diving behind APUs, and generally running for cover. Unbeknownst to us, when Walt applied aft cyclic, the rotor blades struck and destroyed the dorsal fins which sent many pieces flying. We were not, however, aware of this until we shut down.

After conducting some ground tests, we discovered that there were various combinations of collective pitch and cyclic stick that would cause blades-to-vertical fin interference. The flight test team, supported by the AFFTC, recommended grounding all H-43 helicopters pending a solution to the problem. However, we had some difficulty convincing the Weapon System Project Office (WSPO) they should all be grounded.

We finally convinced the WSPO they should at least visit the contractor's facility to observe testing of one of the contractor's proposed interim modifications and further discuss the problem. Initial ground tests consisted of ground taxiing, positioning the helicopter in different nose down attitudes on the ground and moving the controls to various preselected positions. As all the WSPO personnel were observing the test aircraft out the contractor's window, the blades suddenly struck the dorsal fins (sounding

Kaman H-43B after breaking high altitude record.

like a 12 gauge shotgun going off next to your ear) totally destroying the aircraft. The loud noise was because the rotor blades were wooden and shed on impact causing a "slight" unbalanced condition. The H-43 series were immediately grounded. A satisfactory fix was eventually incorporated. As a matter of interest, the initial rotor blades on the Huskie were primarily wood. I had the opportunity one day to visit the rotor blade manufacturing plant and found that a good portion of the production workers were blind. The primary reason for this was the sensitivity of their fingers. They could detect minute flaws during manufacturing and eliminate them.

On another occasion Walt and I were conducting tests at Hartford, Connecticut in preparation of breaking and establishing a new high altitude world record. As usual, we were lost because we had no functional navigation equipment, our heads were in the cockpit, and all that country looks the same. Lots of trees covered with snow.

At 28,500 feet we decided to return home as we were low on oxygen (one walk around bottle each), were cold — no heater, and running low on fuel. Walt called a nearby Air Force Base and Bradley Control (Hartford, Connecticut) to get a fix and then started our descent. The helicopter did not want to smoothly enter a descent; all it wanted to do was "shake, rattle, and roll." What now, coach?

After several attempts using different methods we decided to nose over slightly and rapidly dump collective. Although there were extremely high vibration levels, it worked and we started our descent. During this time frame, the airlines were just starting jet operation and we received numerous comments about "what is a helicopter doing at 28,000 feet?" We did break the world record on December 9, 1959 with Walt and another Air Force pilot at the controls of a fully operational H-43B. The new record was 29,846 feet, beating the old record by nearly 8,000 feet. Two years later the H-43 topped this mark by 2994 feet, pushing the new record to 32,840 feet.

FOILED AGAIN — SOMETHING BROKE
by Don Macpherson

(Article from the L.A. Times, March 13, 1959)
"TWO ABOARD SAFE AFTER COPTER DIVES INTO SEA

"An Army turbine-powered helicopter under Air Force flight test crashed at sea two miles off Santa Barbara yesterday. Two men aboard were rescued by a fishing boat.

"The crewmen were identified as Capt. Walter Hodgson, USAF test pilot and Donald Macpherson, a flight test engineer, both assigned to Edwards Air Force Base, USAF Flight Test Center.

"The Bell Iroquois helicopter was being tested at low altitude over the water. It was being flown temporarily out of Oxnard AFB. Hodgson and Macpherson were returned to Edwards and treated for minor injuries and shock.

"The helicopter sank, but the coastguard will probably attempt to recover it if it can be located."

(1032 hours March 12, 1959)
We were conducting performance testing of the YH-40 U.S. Army Serial No. 56-6724, the prototype for the UH-1 series of Helicopters. The Huey, as it was later called, was redesignated the UH-1 in the mid 1960s. This was flight 55, the second flight of the day, a routine level flight performance test at light gross weight (5150 lb the lightest we could get and still maintain center of gravity) and 314 rotor rpm (the normal operating rotor speed). About 20 minutes into the flight at 80 knots indicated, our fourth test point, in glassy smooth air a mild yaw oscillation was encountered followed by roll and pitch oscillations. The rotor speed was observed to drop rapidly to 230 rpm (285 was the minimum for operation), gas producer speed dropped to about 67% and stabilized, airspeed was reduced to about 70 knots, and a high rate of descent (the needle pegged at -2000 feet per minute) was experienced. The collective pitch control was rapidly lowered to the full down position with

no apparent increase in rate of descent. Rotor speed oscillated slightly between 230 and 240 rpm. A switch to emergency fuel control was made and because of the close proximity to the water, a throttle jam followed with no apparent compressor stall. A flare was attempted by the use of full aft cyclic followed by full up collective with no apparent effect. The aircraft made contact with the water at approximately 60 knots with a high rate of descent.

My memories include placing items on the floor of the helicopter to avoid having them fall on us when we impacted the water. Foiled again... however the aircraft flipped upside down on impact. Fortunately the doors came off. Immediately I struggled to exit the aircraft. Foiled again... I couldn't make it. My attempt finally succeeded when I remembered to unfasten the seat belt. Upon surfacing I pulled the lanyards to inflate the Mae West. Foiled again....the CO_2 cartridges didn't work. I had inflated, by mouth, about one-half of the Mae West, watching the skids disappear from sight and realizing that Walt had not surfaced. I considered deflating my Mae West and trying to dive in an effort to find him. Time appeared to be moving very slowly. Each second seemed like five minutes. Then Walt bobbed up, bleeding freely from his legs, which had been lacerated as he exited through the plexi-glass nose of the aircraft.

On impact Walt had slipped down under the seat belt, forcing his arms upward. As he let out his breath, unable to hold it any longer, enough slack occurred to allow him to slip out of the belt. At that time it was dark inside the aircraft due to its depth. The only light that Walt saw was straight up through the nose and that's where he headed.

I, too, was losing blood from face lacerations. We searched in our emergency kits....Foiled again, the shark repellant could not be found.

We had radioed our impending crash...Foiled again, the combination of low altitude and coastal mountain range blocked the reception. As I was in better condition, I swam away from Walt. This allowed him to use me as the focus to line up the red dot of the signal mirror. The reflection was seen by a fishing boat in the area, and we were rescued from the water and taken to a hospital.

The helicopter was never recovered. The best minds available at the time decided it had been swept off the continental shelf by the current. This news was much to the relief of the Air Force Contracting Officer who had hired commercial salvage operations without complete authorization, payment only to be made upon recovery. This officer was most probably spared from parting with the contents of his bank account.

Part of the return itinerary read "Transportation, boat — Reason for delay, necessary anatomical repairs." The transportation officer at Edwards thought it was some kind of joke.

When asked by Fred Stoliker whether I had lost some of the project data in the crash, I had to confess that... Foiled again, yes, I lost the three data points of the speed-power we were flying.

The cause of the crash was never determined. Subsequent tests by Lycoming and Bell indicated that with approximately one horsepower brake on the engine output shaft the engine would run at the conditions we observed, and the main rotor would recover from rotor speeds well below what we observed. My opinion was that there was a failure in the input drive of the main transmission which caused the transmission to start to bind up not allowing the rotor to accelerate and also producing a slight braking effect on the engine output shaft. The reason for no compressor stall could never be satisfactorily explained.

P.S. After my accident, my Dad wrote to a KFI newscaster (I think his name was Ben Hunter) who used to solicit unusual fish stories. He would air one each week day, select a "winner" and read it on Saturday. The winner would then receive a gift. The story my Dad told went, in part, something like this: "Two men were not having much luck fishing. A strange bird flew over, dove into the ocean, and floundered around. They went over to the scene and using their arms as line and hands as bait pulled two fish from the bloody water." He then briefly described the facts of the accident and signed the letter "The Fish." That week "my" letter was selected and read on Saturday. I received 200 yards of 6 lb test monofilament line and two tickets for an all day deep sea fishing trip out of San Diego. Who says flight test isn't rewarding?

T-33 AIRSTART
by Norris Jay Hanks

Around 1959, significant numbers of T-33 aircraft were being lost when flameouts occurred and airstart attempts were not successful. The many-step airstart procedure, employing many switches, was part of the problem, but also no one knew the altitude/airspeed boundaries of the airstart envelope. An airstart test was authorized and, as Project Officer and Pilot, I was asked to map the starting envelope and to determine a good starting technique.

The engineer assigned was, as I remember, Lou Setter — a brave man who calmly rode through 333 airstart attempts and six deadstick landings, one with a ring of holes around the fuselage behind him made by disintegrated turbine blades. He also came up with the great idea described later.

We eventually made 333 airstart attempts, at altitudes ranging from 500 to 40,000 feet and at airspeeds from stall to maximum permissible. The many attempts were in part because at each altitude the slow and fast limits

Lockheed T-33.

of the start envelope were determined by failures outside and successes inside the envelope. The other variables, besides airspeed and altitude, were windmill RPM and start technique. The procedure was to shut down with extra energy, pass through the aim altitude with stabilized aim airspeed and resulting stabilized windmill RPM and make the start attempt.

At high altitude we often were on instruments because the windshield and canopy fogged and froze almost instantly.

At low altitude it was either get a start or land, with RPM dying and little time for a second try. The electric starter, on battery power, rarely provided enough RPM for a start.

The commanding general of the Flight Test Center did a beautiful job of exactly that. With me in the back seat (with no start capability back there), we finished an evaluation flight including several nice starts at altitude with an attempt at about 1,500 feet on a precautionary downwind leg to the main runway (04). No start. Second try as airspeed and RPM dropped. No start. Add starter. Not enough RPM. Quit and go for the deadstick landing. Grease job. His pulse was not recorded, but the data looked good.

On one flight, when base traffic pushed us across the lakebed to over the bombing range, a similar sequence put me on a final approach over a peninsula sticking out into the lakebed and on to a touchdown among humongus potholes. The tug sent out to fetch us had to be vectored from overhead.

The envelope results were not surprising — a bell shaped area delivering enough windmill RPM and not too much airflow. It turned out that the airspeeds and RPMs on the optimum glide distance profile were fine. That advice could be put in "the book" and could be taught and practiced.

Lou noticed that I had developed a pattern on switch flipping that was most successful. He first suggested creating a hinged bar with differing protrusions at the various switches, so that one "mash" would hit them all, almost simultaneously but in the right order. It worked, after some tailoring, but would require a different, individually tested and tailored bar for each individual aircraft and switch change therein. So the brainstorm — an electric sequencing multi-switch that did them all in proper sequence. Viola! The production model of that "airstart" switch was installed in all T-33s, and, using also the recommended airspeed/altitude profile, the flameout casualty rate dropped to nothing.

The turbine failure occurred somewhere around the 250th start on the same engine. Just plain tired of abuse. The blades missed everything critical and we deadsticked on the lakebed after checking for fire and all controls still working.

§

The X-15 began to expand the realm of manned flight to higher speeds and altitudes, and also to explore methods for controlled reentries from space, through the earth's atmosphere to normal, horizontal landings. In 1960 it achieved Mach 3.3 and an altitude of 136,000 feet.

The Army's use of helicopters and fixed-wing support aircraft was expanding rapidly. It established its own Flight Test Facility at Edwards to evaluate and develop these new weapon systems.

The clandestine flights of the U-2 were brought sharply into the forefront when Francis Gary Powers was shot down over the Soviet Union and captured. In a thinly veiled effort to cover the activity, a U-2 was towed to the hangar at NASA's Flight Research Center. The yellow paint from the recently-applied NASA logo was still wet as it was parked inside. A press conference was held the next morning, and the U-2 was unveiled to the public as a NASA weather research aircraft.

At about the same time, Lockheed's unique "skunk works" was selected to build the next generation of secret surveillance aircraft, the Mach 3-plus A-12.

B-58 MINIMUM CONTROL SPEED TAKEOFFS
by Lt. (then) Charles Haines

In 1960 we were demonstrating takeoffs with loss of an engine, the final planned part of the B-58A Heavyweight Performance Tests. This was the third AFFTC test program on the B-58, the second we had conducted at Edwards, and my first as a Project Engineer. We started on the lakebed, on a place at the very south end called the Ol' Navajo Trail, with taxi tests to develop techniques for controlling the takeoff roll with loss of an engine. Then we moved to the runway for the actual takeoffs, starting at 135,000 pounds and planning to work our way up to max gross weight of 163,000. The test consisted of a normal max AB takeoff roll to refusal speed at which point the pilot chopped an outboard engine, using rudder and nosewheel steering to continue the takeoff.

On the fourth test, at 155,000 pounds, Number 4 was chopped at 148 KIAS. Seconds later I began hearing muffled popping noises - one, then another, then a rapid series. The sounds were barely audible above the roar of the J-79s, but I figured I was hearing blowing tires. Neither of the other

B-58 landing with multiple blown tires.

crew said anything, and I decided to stay quiet until we got off the ground. I had long ago adopted the advice that it's better to go when you can, and stop when you can't. We had the best pilot ever, Fitz Fulton, but we had never discussed this policy and I didn't want to do it in real time. As it turned out, I, in the back seat, was the only one to hear anything or sense anything was wrong until Fitz saw something, probably a tire fragment, fly past him just before rotation.

Liftoff was as planned at 215 KIAS, about 13,000 feet down the runway. I called Fitz immediately, but he had already decided to leave the gear down because of the strange thing he had seen pass him. Everything seemed under control for a few seconds, when he noticed the Primary hydraulic system pressure dropping. We still had the Utility system to give us flight control, but a minute or so later the Utility system indicator also dropped to the peg. I can still remember how quiet the intercom got. I also remember tightening my harness. After several very long seconds Fitz rocked the airplane a few times. He still had control, and we never did lose the Utility system. The Primary system failed of course because shrapnel from the disintegrating wheels and tires damaged the hydraulic lines on the right gear, but we never figured any rational way the incident could have caused the Utility transducer (driving the pressure indicator) to fail. Later generations call such things bad Karma.

Charley Bock, another B-58 pilot, came up in a T-37 to look us over.

The right gear truck was a mess. Seven of the eight tires were missing except for some wire bead, the wheels were ground off, and there were a few holes along the underside. The folks on the ground talked to the folks at General Dynamics, and plans were made to get the airplane back on the ground. The base Flying Safety Officer advised Max (Sgt) Clark and me to eject, but I had once flown with that FSO and had discounted his judgement due to an incident which is another story. Dropping the pod to reduce weight was uneventful, except for worrying about the clearance between the pod and the still extended nose gear. The runway was foamed, we burned down to minimum fuel, jettisoned the second and third station canopies, and landed. The landing was smooth as silk, and rollout seemed pretty normal to me, but during the rollout Charley Bock advised us to not waste time getting out because there was a fair amount of fire following us down the runway. That made sense to me, so the last thing I did before I unplugged my intercom was to challenge Max, in the second station, to see who could get out faster. We had to go down escape ropes because the hatch sills were about 13 or 14 feet off the ground. We had evaluated that rope arrangement earlier, and some of the

General Dynamics B-58 wheel and tire damage following emergency landing.

guys found it tough to do without getting stuck, with their hands caught between the rope and the fuselage. The trick was to use your knees to push your body and the rope away from the fuselage, then let yourself down hand over hand. I got down quickly, and was a good 20 feet ahead of Max when he reached the ground.

The fire stopped as soon as the airplane stopped skidding, and the airplane was eventually patched up enough to be ferried back to General Dynamics for refurb. and conversion to an operational bomber. The only other damage was to my hands, which were nicely burned sliding down my escape rope. I never flew again without gloves, and I've never stopped getting rude comments about this from my Edwards buddies.

(Editor's Note: Former Lt. Haines stopped short of adequately describing the drama of the emergency as the whole base waited for the critical decisions to try to land the airplane with the ground-down wheel hubs. The visual picture is also missing that the movies of the landing show of the massive trail of sparks and fire that followed the aircraft down the runway. It's hard to believe that the rollout seemed normal. One would have expected that the grinding of the aluminum wheel casings would have been heard or felt as vibrations in the aft crew compartment. Lt. Haines' exit from the aft crew compartment was also recorded for history and he truly set a record in descent down a rope. His hands were so badly burned from the

Crew looks at a piece of B-58 tire that blew during takeoff. L to r: Sgt. Max Clark, Lt. Charles Haines, Maj. "Fitz" Fulton. Note Lt. Haines cleverly hiding his burned hands.

friction of the rope that he reported to work for several weeks with his hands totally covered with bandages. He could not even operate the 24-inch slide rule that the flight test engineers used in those days.)

AND THIS BABY WILL ACCELERATE TO 197 MPH
AND STOP IN 2 MILES!
by Rob Ransone Copyright (c) 1995 Ransone Associates, Inc.
Used by permission

Another fun thing about the B-58A was that if you lost an engine on takeoff at, say, about 150 knots, you weren't going fast enough to take off on three engines, but you were going too fast to stop if the drag chute didn't work. No matter how much runway you had left, the brakes could only absorb 18 million foot-pounds of energy each. Period. This left a significant takeoff "deadman's zone" where, if you lost an engine and the drag chute failed, you couldn't takeoff and you couldn't stop. Takeoff speed at maximum weight was 214 knots — "way below" the 217-knot speed at which the quarter inch-thick, 22-inch diameter tires, inflated to 275 psi, would start flying apart at 6000 rpm. The refused takeoff speed had never been demonstrated to the maximum brake limits, so, in November 1960, Fitz Fulton and I got to do it! Our mission: Demonstrate a refused takeoff, at which all four engines are shut down at the three-engine "go speed," and stop without using the drag chute, generating the design brake limit of 18 million foot pounds.

For this program, we used the main runway at Edwards. Our plan was to make a few runs to measure the airplane rolling and air resistance, a run or two to measure the drag chute forces (for which we put strain gauges on the drag chute D-ring), make several runs at increasing brake energies, and investigate the use of aerodynamic braking to slow the airplane to the desired brake energy levels. For the aerodynamic braking test, Fitz would chop the throttles at the desired speed, then raise the nose to increase the drag — which that big delta wing had lots of — and then lower the nose and get on the brakes, while I watched from the chase car. For each test, GD installed new brakes on which we did a low energy "burn-in" run, then parked the airplane at the end of the runway in the run up area and put on new tires. GD had installed "fuse plugs" in each wheel that would melt if the temperature from the brakes got too hot. This would release the air pressure from the tires and prevent them exploding — which could kill a person standing too close or in the wrong position. These normally "popped" about 10 minutes after a moderate energy test run, and we never had a tire explosion. Even though GD had built steel "fenders" over the wheels to protect the airplane from flying debris and fire, both of which we expected, I wanted more safety. Since we were only to accelerate and stop, without actually becoming airborne, I asked GD to replace the fuel with water, except for the small auxiliary tank from which the engines were actually fed. At first, GD was reluctant, but finally agreed. The airplane serial number, 58-1020 was thereafter nicknamed "H2O."

The test airplane was not an instrumented airplane, so we had no onboard data recording equipment. Being an engineer, I wanted to know what was happening, so I asked Instrumentation Branch to install a pressure transducer on the nose gear strut, and a small recorder for this and the strain gauges on the drag chute D-ring. At first, GD was reluctant, but finally agreed when the installation included a hydraulic fuse — I didn't know they made such things, but they did. This simple device provided most remarkable information. Think about it for a moment: The reactions on the nose gear strut as the engines are started and run to power with the brakes set, as they come to military power, then maximum afterburner, the brakes are released, the nose is lifted off, brought back down on the runway, braking is applied very hard, and the airplane comes to a stop with the nose bobbing up and down. I knew everything that was happening on that plane.

One day I noticed that the nose gear seemed to be getting lighter, even though we had not changed the loading. I called the crew chief and asked him to check the balance tank (a small fuel tank in the tail, used for cg control). Sure enough, he found the aft fuel tank valve leaking into the balance tank, shifting the cg aft.

On another occasion, the nose gear didn't load up immediately, as it should have, when Fitz put the nose down. I called Fitz. "Why didn't you streamline the elevons like you were supposed to after you put the nose down?" "How did you know I forgot to do that! You don't have the elevons instrumented."

"Don't ever try to fool your flight test engineer!"

The end of November was getting cold. A couple of nights were freezing. Oops! I called the GD representative.

"Don't we have the aft fuel tank 95% full of water?"

"Yes we do."

"When water freezes, doesn't it expand 10%?"

I had never heard a grown man scream over the telephone before. Thereafter, recording the water temperature was part of the pre-fight checks, and the water was down to 38 degrees F by the time of our last test. On our first, moderate energy test run, a tire started smoking about ten minutes after we stopped, and then burst into flame. The fire department, always standing by for these tests, immediately extinguished the fire, but the fire should not have happened at that energy level. Therefore, I kept the airplane on the main runway until the wheels had cooled enough to examine them closely to see why the problem. Col. MacIntosh, the base maintenance officer, didn't like my keeping the main runway closed for four hours on a good flying morning. He accepted my decision, but threatened: "Pack your mukluks, Lieutenant Ransone — if this happens again, you are off to Thule AFB in Greenland!"

So it was with some trepidation when I had to report to his office and "chew him out" for standing in the wrong place after another test run. I had studied the hazard zones around a tire that explodes. I found from the tire experts that when a tire explodes, it explodes radially in line with the tire, or laterally along the axle line. The safest area is within the four 45-degree wedges between those boundaries. After I advised Col. MacIntosh that he had been in danger, and told him the safe areas, he said: "OK, thanks. You can unpack one of your mukluks."

The day of the big test arrived. It was the last chance we had, because the airplane was scheduled to go into IRAN (Inspect and Repair As Needed – not what you thought, was it?). I had put together the test card that called for maximum power acceleration to 160 KIAS, (the 3-engine "go speed,") shut off all four engines, raise the nose for aerodynamic braking, and then lower the nose and start maximum braking with anti-skid at 140 KIAS to full stop — without a drag chute. It was about 1700 hours (after the day's flying was done, since we were about to close the main runway for several hours), and all of Edwards' brass was on hand to watch.

"Where should we stand?" they asked.

"At 13,500 feet," I answered with confidence.

Then, in typical Hollywood fashion — TROUBLE! The starter cart wouldn't start! We called for another one. The sun was going down. The photo-theodolites had only a few more minutes of daylight.

The tower radioed: "The cart is coming! It just passed the M&M hanger."

The sun kept sinking.

"The cart just passed base ops. It's coming!"

Getting darker!

"The cart is at the plane!"

Engine start! Preflight! Taxi into position. Cameras ready. Fire trucks — every truck on the base — ready. The bosses waiting at 13,500 feet. Chase car ready. Fitz's countdown: "Military power. Check. Afterburner light off. Check. Full power...now. Check. 5...4...3...2...1...brake release."

With the last orange rays of the setting sun glinting off its sides, the beautiful plane roared down the runway. "Engine chop...nose up." In the chase car, we were in hot pursuit. "140 knots...nose down...full brakes!"

Fitz brought the plane to a smooth stop, with tires bursting into flame, fire trucks roaring up and their crews scrambling out to foam the wheels, and Fitz clamoring down the escape rope, all within 76 feet of the spectators! God! What a sight!

It could have been even more spectacular. As the plane came to a stop, the aft fuel tank high level shutoff failed, and the tank vented large quantities, cascading down over the wing, hissing onto the wheel fires. Quantities — not of fuel — but water. H_2O.

THE B-58 NON-FRANGIBLE WHEEL
by Jim Ford

I thought I'd gotten away from the B-58 and all its problems when I was transferred from Carswell AFB to Edwards AFB in the fall of 1960. Guess it just wasn't to be!

While working as a two-striper engineering and scientific aide for Doolittle Raider Col David M. Jones and the B-58 Test Force at Carswell, I became involved in the data analysis effort associated with a serious main landing gear wheel problem. Because the B-58 wing was very thin, there was not much room for the main landing gear to rotate and stow in the up position. In order to stay within the available space in the wing and still meet the load requirements, General dynamics designed and built a four-axle bogie with two small wheels per axle, for a total of eight on each main gear. These small, heavily-loaded wheels reached a very high rotational speed compared to those on other large aircraft. During test operations from the Carswell runway, several incidents involving tire failure at heavy gross weight resulted in serious damage to the aircraft. One incident occurred during a heavy weight takeoff which cost the lives of two crewmen in addition to total aircraft loss. We narrowed the cause to tire overloading and failure during the takeoff roll. Thus, development of a non-frangible wheel configuration was initiated.

By destiny, my first assignment at Edwards was to test the newly-designed non-frangible wheel on the Edwards B-58 test aircraft. A non-frangible center flange was to be installed between the two wheels on each axle, in place of the normal wheel spacer. This unique, solid metal "third wheel" was larger in diameter than the adjacent wheel rims. It was supposed to carry the axle load, without breaking apart, in the event tires on both wheels of that axle failed during a takeoff or landing roll. For the test program, a special, shielded axle beam assembly with only a single test wheel assembly

The B-58 non-frangible wheel.

and steel skids was installed in the aft section of the landing gear strut.

My pilot was Maj. Fitz Fulton, and my contractor counterpart was senior design engineer Byron Anderson of General Dynamics-Ft Worth, who designed both the B-58 and the F-16 landing gear systems. During the early development phase, we tested various wheel bearing configurations to see which one would best withstand the shock of a metal wheel rolling on a concrete surface. On test days, we would follow the B-58 out to the end of runway 22 for a test run at 0600 hours (in those days we could drive our own cars on the flightline). After parking our cars a safe distance from the main runway, Byron and I hopped into fire chief Actis' pickup and sped down runway 04 after the B-58 as it accelerated to the designated taxi speed. We did this in an attempt to further determine the sequence of events if the wheel bearings came apart and the parts were scattered along the runway (which they did during many of the early test runs). Our runway cameras simply would not cover enough area to see it all! When this happened, Byron and I trudged back down the runway picking up the parts and logging their condition and location by hand.

When we finally found a suitable bearing configuration, we began high speed taxi tests with several aluminum center flanges of varying hardness to find the best wheel configuration. To make the test as realistic as possible, we installed custom made (courtesy of General Dynamics) 20mm projectile guns in the protective shield, with a switch in the cockpit to allow the pilot to blow the tires after starting a takeoff roll. Fitz was the only test pilot I know of who had the fortitude to blow out his own tires in the interest of furthering our knowledge in test and evaluation! After finding the best wheel configuration, we mounted a complete brake assembly on top of the shield and a production anti-skid system in the test wheel so we could do some braking tests. By then, the airfield manager was getting more than a little peeved at us for tying up the main runway with our dumb tests, and he began scheduling us after normal duty hours. One test in particular was a high energy braking run which flattened the tires, ground away half of the shield and steel skids, and fused the brake stack into a solid, burned-up mass. The B-58 had finally come to a stop about 2000 feet short of the East taxiway after rolling more than 11,000 feet down runway 04. About three hours later, after dark, we were still helping the maintenance crew get the mess cleaned up and the wheel changed so we could tow the plane back to the M&M hangar. Suddenly, we heard the sound of engines and looked up just in time to see a B-52 making a landing approach right at us!! We immediately dropped tools and frantically scattered to the side of the runway as he passed over us to a touchdown — his landing gear missed the B-58 tail by about 25 feet. Needless to say, the guy in the tower caught heck for lack of communication with the B-52 about the runway condition not being cleared for landing.

Our final test was a takeoff at 227 KIAS after the pilot blew his tires and rolled more than 10,000 feet on the center flange. He landed at 145 KIAS and rolled another 13,000 feet without incident. The wheel was subsequently retrofitted on all B-58 aircraft in the field. I received the AFFTC Airman-Of-The-Month award for December 1960 as project engineer on this program. Fitz later retired from the Air Force and went to work for NASA. Most folks at Edwards know his achievements as a NASA pilot after that.

ON THE RUNWAY
by Charles E. Kroll

After several interesting and exciting flight evaluations (C-123J, F-27, YC-134), I was once again assigned a large Edwards-based flight test program: the C-130B Category II Performance Tests. I much preferred the flight evaluations since they were short (my first project was to finish Lt. Dave Leisy's F-100D Category II Performance tests which had nearly 100 different external store configurations; talk about getting data to cross plot) and more importantly occurred before the contractor had sold the aircraft to the Air Force, so he was more supportive, especially if the test program was at the contractor's facility. Data reduction resources were at your beck and call whereas at

Lockheed C-130B "Hercules."

Edwards it was tough competition to get data reduction support. Prior to 1960, Air Force Performance and Flying Quality test program aircraft were instrumented with photo panels and oscillographs with their attendant manual data reduction methods. Contractors at times used telemetry instrumentation for early safety of flight programs. The C-130B was to be Eddy's first attempt to use the new magnetic tape instrumentation technology. Al Phillips had moved from the Performance Engineering Branch to head the Data Reduction Branch in Technical Support, and had finally convinced Fred Stoliker (a diehard photo panel and oscillograph advocate) to use the new magnetic tape instrumentation technology. And I was selected to be the flight test engineer for this technology transition program.

The test pilot was Captain Jack "COWBOY" Allavie whose favorite maneuver was to make an unannounced high speed run over the runway and then call the tower, "526 on the break." Tower operators would frantically search the sky looking for a fighter aircraft, only to see our C-130 that should have been making a conventional down-wind, base-leg, final approach. Another favorite was to touch down right at the lake bed end of Runway 22, turn off at the east taxiway, and wave to all the oncoming aircraft which were taxiing out for take off.

We had completed the program except for the heavyweight takeoffs and landings. The cargo compartment was filled with a 14 tank water ballast system with dump and transfer provisions for weight and center of gravity control in flight. We were scheduled to do heavyweight takeoffs and landings. I was up front standing behind the pilot's seat to read the 50-foot and touchdown airspeeds from the pilot's panel; Lt. Charles O. Johnson was back at one of the test engineer's stations at the back of the aircraft (getting his flying time for flight pay as a tech observer); and Al Phillips was seated in the other test engineers' seat to observe his magnetic tape system in operation. Captain Allavie set up the approach and everything seemed in order. I read and recorded the 50 foot airspeed. As we approached touchdown Jack pulled the stick back, first gradually and then all the way into his gut. The nose came up as it should have but we impacted with a loud "CRUNCH." My knees buckled and I fell to the floor not having seen, much less read and recorded, our touchdown airspeed. As I was picking myself up, Jack called over the intercom, "Is every one OK in the back?" After a short silence, Charlie Johnson came back over the intercom with, "Well sir, we've either ruptured the water ballast tanks or else Mr. Phillips has wet his pants." After taxiing in, maintenance inspected the aircraft. Several water ballast tanks had ruptured and we leaked water all the way to the parking ramp.

With the maximum gross weight condition, even though there was adequate elevator effectiveness to rotate the aircraft, the wing was definitely lift limited so we essentially rotated but never flared. Initial contact with the runway was at the lower ramp door hinge line aft of the main landing gear. AFFTC Maintenance did a good job of repairing the tanks but because of the delay we published the Performance Category II Tests in April without the takeoff and landing results. They were published later in an Addendum.

BUDDY AERIAL REFUELING
by Norris Jay Hanks

Around 1960, we did a test of the "Buddy Refueling" system, for the F-100 and the F-101 (the Navy had a similar system), where a "Strike Aircraft", loaded with armament, and a "Buddy" aircraft, with a large external tank that included an extendable fuel hose and drogue, would depart from friendly territory and head out. As they approached the target, the strike fighter refueled from the buddy and pressed on to hit the enemy while the buddy turned and refueled from a tanker, to the rear, and then returned to meet the striker on his way home. It was my program, but I had never refueled before.

Another factor in the test was a new, untested, refueling probe for the F-100 — straight forward from the wing in the past, bent up and then forward in the new configuration to place the probe higher in the pilot's view and make the "plug in" easier.

I thought it would be advisable for me to make at least one refueling from a regular tanker, with drogue trailing from a wing tip, in order to compare the regular with the Buddy system. Before the first Buddy test, I managed to get scheduled onto a tanker out of Nellis, but only on a "non-interference basis." In the F-100 with the "bent probe", I flew out to meet and hang around the tanker near Nellis, while a series of tactical flights rendezvoused, refueled and left. My fuel kept getting lower and darkness came on while I waited. Finally, I had to either refuel or go home, now.

With a tanker crew member in the waist watching my first try ever, I had that drogue everywhere on my airplane except on the probe. Finally, I stabbed it but with a glancing blow. The old probe had been straight with no rotary forces and was mounted with no lock to prevent rotation. This new one, also unstaked in rotation, promptly rotated to place the probe down, completely out of sight to me, and then disconnected.

Perhaps it was better down there. With darkness upon us, the waist "gunner" talked me in with an "up, down, right, left" series to "plug it", after which I flew formation on the wing tip until flow ceased.

The buddy tests proceeded to satisfactory conclusions, including refuelings from F-100 to F-101, vice versa, etc. My next refueling from a large tanker was from a KC-135, years later, off the coast of North Vietnam, again with an F-100 but with a staked probe. But that is another story.

T-38 TIREBLOW
by Norris Jay Hanks

The early T-38 test effort, around 1960, was divided into characteristics (performance, stability and control, etc.) tests and operational (maintenance, training, etc.) tests, with different engineers, pilots, and jargons for each group. Although I was part of the characteristics group, one time, when the operational group needed some help, I flew a maximum braking, stop and go landing card that aligned fuel remaining numbers with test landing speed. After about four stop and gos, with landing gear retracted and a rectangular pattern in between each, I was on the downwind leg when one tire blew in its wheel well. After some consultations and some checks by a chase aircraft, I put the gear down, the runway was foamed and I landed with the blown tire sliding in the foam, losing directional control only during the last few feet of the roll. The problem was caused by jargon difference. The T-38 had left and right fuel tanks and gages. The operational group combined the sides to a single total "reading" while the characteristics group called the two sides separately. I had landed each time with exactly twice the "designated amount of fuel.

Northrop T-38 "Talon."

No one previously had blown a tire. I had blown one and not blown the other — a perfect data point, exactly on the envelope.

THE X-20 (DYNA SOAR) SIMULATOR
by Frank Anderton

(Editors' note: The X-20 was to be a continuation of the "X" series of high speed research airplanes. It was sponsored and funded primarily by the Air Force with expected flight test participation by NASA. The X-20 was a delta-winged glider that was initially to be launched vertically on top of an ICBM-class booster from Cape Canaveral. It would then perform a reentry and glide to a landing on one of the Caribbean Islands or on the coast of Brazil. Boeing was selected to build the glider. As bigger and better boosters became available, the Dyna Soar concept expanded to include orbital flights to Edwards. The first airplane was under construction at Boeing and flight test planning was well under way at the time of the first X-15 powered flight in 1960.)

Experience with the X-15 program convinced all of us working on the X-20 that a flight test simulator was essential to a safe and efficient flight test program. We also realized that computer technology of the early 1960s was unable to meet the difficult challenge of the X-20. Digital technology of those days was not fast enough to compute vehicle pitch, roll and yaw responses in real time. At the same time, analog computers, which could handle the stability and control problem with ease, were not capable of repeatable, accurate solutions of the long term trajectory equations which, for a single orbit flight, took two hours in real time.

Very early in the program, before 1960, we had set up the trajectory equations on an old analog computer belonging to the Engineering Division and got better results than we expected. Our first attempts were not good because the solution was extremely sensitive to errors made when the vehicle speed was close to orbital speed. Even something as innocent sounding as amplifier drift, which our prehistoric computer had big time, could easily ruin the solution. We got a good break when Capt. Joe Bulger, the Chief of our Simulator Lab., put us in touch with Bob Howe of the University of Michigan who had developed a set of equations optimized for solving the trajectory on an analog computer. These equations used the equilibrium orbital speed as the reference speed (instead of zero) thereby reducing sensitivity to error by a couple of orders of magnitude. These equations made an enormous difference and we were actually able to get usable (but not very accurate and not very repeatable) results from our antique computer.

We believed that with good state of the art equipment and special error-limiting procedures, we could achieve a high accuracy even over a two hour real-time period. Part of our belief came from a conviction that we really had to make it work. Some industry people familiar with analog simu-

Boeing X-20 "Dyna Soar" mockup.

lation said it was impossible.

The Center was scheduled for a new simulator, so we scouted around and finally decided that EAI of Princeton, NJ had what we needed. A special electrical ground system was installed (a sizeable "well" behind the building with continuous dripping water) and we spent many hours calibrating the amplifiers. We checked each amplifier for drift and finally selected the best of them to solve the trajectory equations. We also employed variable scaling and other skullduggery to minimize error. In the end we achieved a simulator that would repeatedly fly a 21,000 mile trajectory with an error of less than 30 miles.

Although we did some pioneering research efforts on the X-20 simulator we never got a chance to really give it a workout because the X-20 was cancelled in 1963 before reaching the flight stage. Shortly after X-20 cancellation the excellent analog computation facility was modified with a digital computer which was tied to the analog to make a hybrid computer. The hybrid system was used to simulate many other aircraft in support of AFFTC flight test programs.

§

The Soviet Union again shocked the U.S. scientific community by launching Yuri Gagarin aboard the Vostok I to became the first man to orbit the earth. Alan Shepard rode the first manned flight of NASA's Mercury capsule to an altitude of 615,000 feet in a short, 302-mile flight down the Atlantic missile range.

President Kennedy, in a bold move to regain scientific prestige, committed the U.S. to landing a man on the moon before 1970, thus the Apollo Program was born.

Although the X-15 program was conceived long before the start of the "space race", it was now playing an important role in upholding the U.S. lead in aviation while gathering data in the space environment and demonstrating the operation of various subsystems at zero "g". The X-15 was never officially assigned a high military priority at Edwards. Each flight attempt, (usually 3 or 4 per month), required a massive amount of AF and NASA support — chase aircraft, radar, fire trucks, paramedics, etc. No one wanted to be the "bad guy" responsible for cancelling an X-15 flight, so many rules and schedules for other Edwards activities were "bent slightly" to accommodate the needed support.

With this unofficial support from the entire flight test community at Edwards, the X-15 continued its deliberate expansion of the envelope of piloted flight, achieving 6 times the speed of sound and an altitude of slightly over 200,000 feet in 1961.

FLIGHT TESTING THE B-58 HUSTLER
by Clendon L. Hendrickson

Most of us came to Edwards AFB because we wanted to work on the development, test, and evaluation of the new, modified, and research aircraft being tested there. Edwards had the additional attraction of being one of the few places on earth where a civilian could fly in these high performance, state-of-the-art airplanes.

I arrived at Edwards in January 1961 with a brand new sheepskin in Aeronautical Engineering from the University of Washington. Being interested in supersonic aircraft, I was fortunate enough to be assigned to the B-

General Dynamics' B-58 "Hustler."

58 program. This aircraft was a large, 163,000-pound, four-engine, delta-winged bomber designed to carry nuclear weapons at speeds up to Mach 2 and deliver them to any point on the globe.

After about six months, I was ready to fly and was fortunate enough to fly with Major Fitzhugh Fulton, who was one of the best, if not the best, engineering test pilots in the business. The flight consisted of a climb and descent to the ocean and then constant Weight/Altitude Pressure Ratio (W/Delta) speed power points to develop pilot handbook cruise data for the airplane. I might add here that, in those days, we used slide rules for calculations and fuel management and I suspect it pretty much resembled the old one-armed paper hanger in the back seat. This involved monitoring the fuel flow meters and estimating the fuel used during a test point, calculating the gross weight, then using a constant W/Delta, calculating the altitude for the next point, which was usually a couple hundred feet higher and 20 or 30 knots slower.

As we arrived over the ocean, Fitz said "There is a cloud bank over the water, how low do you want to go?" With all my inexperience I answered "Just as low as you can get." As we leveled off approximately 200 feet above the water, the altimeter read –350 feet (due to pitot-static system position error) and the aircraft was stabilized for the first point at 630 knots. The data was turned on for one minute and the calculation began for the next point. When I had finished my calculation and had given it to the pilot, he said "data on." I looked up and he was already stabilized at the proper altitude and airspeed. Didn't I say before that I was fortunate? It occurred to me that there might be a fishing boat, patrol boat, or sail boat under that overcast that must have gotten a real boom as that big aircraft passed over at 200 feet with all four engines roaring.

In those days we used a photo panel with a 400-foot roll of 35mm film that took pictures of the instrument panel in the back cockpit. This film was later read for the performance parameters and the data calculated using slide rules and mechanical Olivetti (Thrashing Machine) calculators, then hand plotted on the back side of green Vellum graph paper. The curves were drawn using plastic curves that fit the data points best. Cross checks were always made using drag polars and other data to ensure that the fairings were compatible. After all the data had been gathered and analyzed to determine how satisfactorily the aircraft met, or failed to meet, the specifications, a technical report was written on the results.

On another occasion, I was called upon to fly in one of the aircraft that had the canopy removed from the second station and modified to accommodate a clamshell escape capsule to be used during ejection at high speeds. On this flight, the pilot was Major Jack Allavie, who was very jovial on the ground, but all business in the cockpit. The cockpits were extremely cold, with snow coming out of the air-conditioning ducts, which Jack could not do anything about. During the 600-knot portion of the climb, we experienced severe vibration, which shook many of the porcelain fuses out of the panels in the back seat. At first I tried to replace them, but there soon became so many I feared putting them in the wrong place and stopped trying to replace them. As we reached 44,000 feet, Jack lit the afterburners and quickly accelerated the aircraft to Mach 2. During this acceleration, I heard a very high pitched vibration, almost a scream, and then the aircraft was decelerated, descended and landed. The second station was a shambles. The web of the two large "I" beams that were to be used for the ejection seat rails had failed and the flanges bent sidewise in the cockpit. The instrumentation wiring was loose and the whole cockpit was in disarray. Needless to say, considerable modification was required before the planned ejections were conducted. Incidentally, after that flight I received a Mach 2 pin, which I still have, and membership in the Mach 2 Club, which in the early sixties was a pretty exclusive group. Escape capsules were eventually ejected at very high speeds with chimpanzees and bears in them and the program was declared a success.

On another occasion we were to deliver an aircraft back to the General Dynamics factory at Fort Worth, Texas. Major Ken Lewis was the pilot, Don Gobert was in the second cockpit as flying qualities engineer, and I was in the back looking after performance test points. Tests conducted during the flight were to include lateral stability, which consisted primarily of aileron rolls. The procedure was 1/4 stick, 1/2 stick, 3/4 stick, and full stick, both left and right, at a given airspeed and altitude, and then repeated at a different set of conditions. I might add here that I consider Don Gobert to be one of the most versatile and capable engineers we had at that time and with the tenacity of a bulldog. The oxygen system in the B-58 was a full pressure system and at altitude it was quite difficult to talk against the pressure. Don, being soft-spoken anyway, wasn't always easy to understand on the intercom system. After a long series of rolls, Ken asked, "How was that?" and Don mumbled something unintelligible. We flew along straight and level for a while, and I saw something running down the floor of the aircraft. I said, "I think he's sick." Pretty soon Don came back on the intercom and said, "We need to do them again." What did I say about tenacity? Any airliners that observed us rolling across country must have thought it was a frivolous expenditure of the taxpayers money.

BIRTH OF THE USAF AEROSPACE RESEARCH PILOT CLASS
by Bill Schweikhard

I started my career in flight testing as a flight test engineer at the Air Force Flight Test Center where I was initially a civilian, then two years as an Air Force Officer, and then once again a civilian employee of the US Air Force. During this time at Edwards, 1955 to 1959, I had been involved in the flight testing of fighter airplanes including the F-86D, F-100, F/TF-102, and F-104. My test pilot for the TF-102 was Deke Slayton of the original Mercury Astronaut selection. Needless to say I had an intense interest in space and astronautics and was reading and learning everything I could about astronautics.

A new civilian position was opened at the USAF Test Pilot School for someone to upgrade the curriculum with modern methods and training materials. They were looking for a flight test engineer with recent test experience. When I interviewed for the position I asked if they intended to provide initial training for astronauts. The commandant, Col. Leonhart, emphatically answered "NO!" They selected me anyway. I was careful not to bring up the subject again during his tour of duty. In the meantime, during my off duty hours, I proceeded to lay out an Astronaut-related curriculum as I thought it should be done and talked to other instructors who were of a similar mind. Two of these were Tom Stafford and Ed Givens — both of whom later became Gemini and Apollo Astronauts. Givens was selected but was killed in a car accident before he ever flew.

Lt. Col. Dick Lathrop succeeded Col. Leonhart as Commandant and recognized the need to investigate Astronaut training possibilities. So I pulled out my personal "Astronaut Training" file and began improving on it. Lt. Col. "Moke" Howe replaced Dick and was very receptive to the Astronaut Training Program idea and aggressively pursued it by authorizing Major Tom McElmurry (a test pilot) and me (a flight test engineer) to travel to government, industry, academia and other organizations to gather all information available to develop such a program at the Test Pilot School. No University in the free world had anything more than one or two courses that might apply. There was no budget and no authorization for this effort. We were given a T-33 airplane, a credit card to buy fuel and a one page set of orders authorizing us to travel for this purpose. The rest was out of our pocket. So we used the messes at military installations and the visiting officers' quarters at $4 per night. We spent the better part of six months traveling, talking to everyone and anyone who would listen and help.

At home we were given a spare class room and a couple of desks. This became our headquarters from which we prepared our proposal which we would present to higher headquarters. Gaining local approval was relatively easy but from there on the going got tough. After numerous presentations at the Air Research and Development Command Headquarters at Andrews Air Force Base near Washington and at the Pentagon, we were getting a bit discouraged. Undaunted we pressed on, presenting it to anyone who would listen. Finally someone at the Chief of Staff level started asking what the military was doing where manned space flight was concerned. Some-

First Aerospace Research Pilot class. L to r: Lt. Col. "Moke" Howe, Bill Schweikhard, Maj. Jim McDivitt, Tom McElmurry, Maj. Frank Borman, Maj. "Buck" Buchanan.

one volunteered that there were some people walking the halls of the Pentagon with a proposal for training Astronaut candidates. They invited us in to the high level conference rooms and bought into our proposal. From then on we were on our way.

We were authorized the funds to procure the sophisticated ground and flight training equipment, much of which existed only in our heads and had never before been designed or built. The problem was that AF Headquarters wanted results immediately. That is, they wanted the first class to graduate tomorrow if possible. So we set up the academic program and lashed together hands-on training using existing NASA and industry research simulators, borrowed high performance airplanes that the school didn't have, used the Brooks Medical Center's biomedical training expertise to specially concoct the medical training part of the program, and then volunteered as test subjects for a high-g experiment at the Navy's Johnsville centrifuge that the NASA Astronauts were unable to support. The curriculum was finalized there in a motel at Warminster, PA. I contributed my flight testing engineering experience plus some knowledge of orbital mechanics and rocketry that I had acquired on my own. The test pilots contributed their flying experience and knowledge of pressure suits, subsystems, and training methods. Even the academics, which were my primary responsibility, were not easily put in a polished form in such a short time. The course sessions were held over the entire United States. The original plan called for the course to be presented to uninitiated test pilots who knew nothing about space flight. There was no time for a NASA-type selection process and, even if there were, the course was not ready for students who did not already have some knowledge of the subject. In a "depths of despair" meeting to review the progress and status of the course, I suggested that the first class consist of the initial instructors who were on board at that time, and one or two highly qualified test pilots from Edwards to critique the curriculum as it existed. Jim McDivitt was the one outsider who was included.

Those who were there from the very beginning were McElmurry and myself, followed by Borman and finally Buchanan. These, plus McDivitt, made up the first Astronaut Training Class. Notice that it consisted of 4 test pilots and one flight test engineer. Tom Stafford and Ed Givens were already there as instructors in the Test Pilot Training Program.

Some of the more notable names in the test piloting business of the day found their way to the school later as part of the classes (Pete Knight, X-15 Astronaut), and, still later, as commandant was Chuck Yeager, (X-1 first supersonic flight), Buzz Aldrin, (Gemini/Apollo 11), et al.

X-15: VENTRAL-OFF
by Bob Hoey

I was assigned as the Air Force Flight Planner during the X-15 envelope expansion program. This was my first experience with a research airplane, but my counterpart from NACA, Dick Day, had been involved in the X-2, X-3, and several other research vehicles. All flight planning for the X-15 envelope expansion was heavily dependent on the 6-degree-of-freedom simulator which was a relatively new tool in the flight testing business. We learned early-on from the simulator that the best method for accomplishing a successful reentry from high altitude was to establish a constant angle of attack quite early in the descent, then allow the g to build as the dynamic pressure increased. When the maximum desired g was reached (usually 5.5 g) angle of attack was gradually decreased in order to maintain a constant g. Maximum dynamic pressure was usually reached just prior to achieving level flight, and the angle of attack was then further reduced to perform a one g level deceleration. The higher the value of peak altitude, the higher the value of initial angle of attack required to avoid exceeding the aircraft structural limits.

Shortly after the centrifuge program in mid 1958, (and very close to the rollout date for the first airplane) there was an update to the aerodynamic data used in the simulation. Earlier lateral-directional data had been based on wind tunnel runs with the horizontal stabilizer at zero deflection. The

North American X-15 without ventral fin, ready to launch from NB-52 mothership.

update included more recent wind tunnel runs which had identified the lateral-directional effects of non-zero stabilizer deflections. The news was not good! Previous simulation studies had predicted that reentries with the stability augmentation system (SAS) off were possible using an initial angle of attack of 15 degrees. Above that angle of attack a strong pilot-induced-oscillation (PIO) developed and the airplane was uncontrollable without the SAS. Simulation studies after the update showed that the maximum controllable reentry angle of attack was now only 8 degrees! This was barely adequate to perform an entry from 200,000 feet altitude, and was totally inadequate for an entry from the design altitude of 250,000 feet. Further simulator studies showed that the roll damper was the critical feature needed to retain control.

The X-15 was originally equipped with a dual, fail-safe SAS system consisting of a working channel and a monitor channel in each axis. When a difference was detected between the working and monitor channels in any axis, that channel merely shut itself off. If our simulator was correct, this meant that for any flight above 200,000 feet, a single failure in the roll SAS channel would result in the loss of the airplane.

The first step toward resolving this problem was to verify that the problem was real and not some quirk in the simulation. In Aug 1960, on a Mach 3+ flight (while still using the small XLR-11 engines) we had the pilot intentionally turn the roll SAS off, then increase the angle of attack. The resulting divergent lateral oscillations were identical to what we had seen on the simulator.

The problem was caused by the adverse rolling moment created by the large ventral fin. Although the airplane had plenty of directional stability, the dihedral effect was strongly negative at the higher angles of attack (i.e., left sideslip produced left roll). After flying the roll-SAS-off flight mentioned above, Joe Walker described the sensation as "like a marble rolling on the OUTSIDE of a barrel." (The standard text-book description of "Dutch roll" motions relates it to a marble rolling on the INSIDE of a barrel).

The initial reaction from most of the stability and control community at North American and NASA was to design and build a backup roll damper. Before long, work had started on the Auxiliary Stability Augmentation System (ASAS). Dick and I felt that something more was needed. The simulation really didn't fly that well even when all dampers were operating normally, especially when trying to set up an entry from high altitude. We sought an aerodynamic fix and began to explore what might happen if we simply removed the ventral fin. Although there was a lot of subsonic data with the ventral off (it was jettisoned before every landing), there was only one set of supersonic wind tunnel runs at Mach 3 without the ventral. Dick and I created a temporary modification to the simulation using this data and some freehand guesses to fill in the missing holes at other Mach numbers. The directional stability was considerably less, but the dihedral effect was normal at all angles of attack and the Dutch Roll stability was about the same. The simulation was now easily controlled with the SAS off and entries from 250,000 feet were stable all the way down. We had enough confidence in our ventral-off predictions that we proposed a low speed (Mach 4), low altitude (80,000 feet) flight. (Everything is relative!) We presented the concept to the rest of the technical folks at NASA and most thought that we would need a complete new set of wind tunnel data (which would take a couple of years and a lot of money) before they would even consider such a flight. Paul Bikle, the Director of NASA Dryden, and Bob Rushworth, the Air Force X-15 test pilot, were a little more understanding of our idea. They saw the logic in what we were proposing and allowed us to lay out plans for a "safe" flight with the ventral off to prove the concept and thus place a higher priority on obtaining new ventral-off wind tunnel data.

The first ventral-off flight was to be flown by Major Bob Rushworth on Oct. 4, 1961. As the flight day approached Dick and I became more and more nervous. We knew our hypothesis was based on some pretty thin evidence. After all, the vertical tail area on nearly all of the Century-Series fighters had to be INCREASED by 15 to 20 percent following initial supersonic flights. We were preparing to DECREASE the vertical tail area of the X-15 by 27 percent! We had devised a completely different set of gain settings for the SAS based on the ventral-off aerodynamic predictions. Our selected roll gain was "2", only 1/3 of the normal ventral-on setting of "6". We had no idea what stability degradation might occur due to rocket plume effects while the engine was running. We had no data on the effects of speed brake deflection. We really worked hard on the simulator during that last week, "what-if-ing" the entire flight and trying to devise alternate courses of action for some of the "more remote" possibilities. At the same time, we were continually reassuring Rushworth that we really did have confidence in the simulation and in our own aerodynamic predictions. On the morning of the flight I suspect that Bikle and Rushworth had more confidence in Hoey and Day than did Hoey and Day.

The first ventral-off flight was letter perfect! Handling qualities were similar to the ventral-on configuration at low angles of attack, but better at 8 degrees angle of attack. Several stability pulses were performed which confirmed the trends of our predictions. We had successfully made our case. There was an immediate move to obtain "real" wind tunnel data on the ventral-off configuration over the entire speed range.

The ASAS was installed in April 1962 and Joe Walker flew the first flight to nearly the design altitude (247,000 feet) on April 30, 1962 with the ventral on, and the ASAS installed. There were no further ventral-on high altitude flights except for a few in ship #3 which had a triply-redundant, self-adaptive control system. Five months later the ventral-off wind tunnel data had been completed and mechanized on the simulator. The second ventral-off flight (with much less stress for the flight planners) was flown on Sept 28, 1962. All subsequent flights of all three X-15's were flown in the ventral-off configuration, including the flight to the highest altitude, 354,200 feet. It proved to be a superior aerodynamic configuration and allowed reentries to be performed routinely at 25 degrees angle of attack. Wind tunnel data did show us that the directional stability transonically with the speed brakes out was negative, and we carefully briefed the pilots on how to avoid that area. Those were times when it was OK to take a risk, and Paul Bikle and Bob Rushworth took a BIG risk by trusting in the instincts and abilities of a couple of flight test engineers.

§

John Glenn orbited the earth in Mercury 6. Although we were playing "catch-up", this was the beginning of a very ambitious U.S. manned space flight program.

Still under very tight secrecy, Lockheed's A-12 (the forerunner of the SR-71 "Blackbird") made its first flight.

The X-15 flown by Maj. Bob White reached an altitude of over 300,000 feet .

PROJECT ROUGH ROAD ALPHA
by Jack Westphal

Suddenly one Sunday in July 1962 Major Joe Marling invited me to drop by his house. I was told I was the Test Director for Project Rough Road Alpha. The purpose of this high priority program was to determine the maximum takeoff and landing performance of five aircraft from unprepared surfaces with the minimum bearing strength capable of supporting the test aircraft. The US Army also had a requirement to fly a 20,000 lb payload 500 NM, land on this minimum surface, and then bring it back.

The test aircraft were a standard C-130B (S/N 61-2649); a modified JC-130B (S/N 57-0525) with 50 degrees of flaps and higher propeller speeds; the boundary control NC-130B (S/N 58-0712), a YC-123H (S/N 54-2956) with modified landing gear, braking parachutes and two CJ-610-1 turbojets; and a standard C-123B (S/N 54-0662).

The supporting test force team were Cpt. Tommy I. Bell (ASD) as my assistant test director; 1/Lt. Ray Johnson, chief engineer succeeded by Clen Hendrickson; flight test engineers 1/Lt. Tom Wright and Capt. Bill Mackey - C-130B, Clen Hendrickson - JC-130B, Capt. Rob Ransone - NC-130B, 2/Lt. Harold Swanson - C-123B, and Capt. Matt Murphy - YC-123H. All these were AFFTC engineers. 1/Lt. Art Steczkowski (ASD) was the YC-123H lead engineer. The test pilots were Capt. Bill Loewe - C-130B, Maj. Joe Shiele - JC-130B and C-123B from AFFTC; and Maj. Ed Wilson - NC-130B and Capt. Dick Bearman - YC-123H from ASD.

In addition the project had excellent support from the base Civil Engineers siting runways and Fairchild cameras; base supply getting replacement engines, props, brakes, etc.; the maintenance group changing engines and props at Yuma and getting the NC-130 out of too soft mud at Harpers Lake; and Al Phillips' Tech Support outfit for Askania and Fairchild camera coverage and data reduction.

Ray Johnson on the preceding Rough Road program had found that sharp sand and soft clay were the minimum bearing surfaces from which we could operate. We were blessed in that Jack Strier was running a test of B-47s and B-52s from dry lakebeds. He had three US Army soils engineers assigned which I commandeered to find test sites. These folks soon found a suitable sand site next to the Yuma MCAS runway and, after some misadventure, a wet clay site at Harpers Dry Lake east of Edwards. I had tried in vain to build a clay site between the Edwards main runway and Lake Rosamond. Some wag put up an arrow labelled "Schiele Field." Joe was upset; thought it should be named after me.

We ran baseline tests on all the test aircraft on the Edwards runway before going to the selected sites. The C-130B, JC-130B and the YC-123H were tested first at Yuma. Since sand is tough on airplanes all takeoff tests were completed first. Takeoffs from sand were followed by landing on the main runway. Landings in sand were to bear out this procedure: the 130B broke a bulkhead supporting the landing gear and needed four engines replaced for sand erosion; the YC-123H needed props and tires replaced - and the JC-130B broke both bulkheads and a major gear support. The JC was ok'd for a flight to the depot; lost an engine on the way and never returned to the program. Wising up, I finished testing the NC-130B and the C-123B at Harpers Lake before venturing into the sand. I also limited the NC-130 to a maximum gross weight of 115,000 lb in sand tests.

The test results were pretty spectacular for all except the C-123B. For the US Army 20,000 lb payload, the gross weight at landing and takeoff was 101,000 for the 130s and 62,000 lb for the YC-123H. The C-123B couldn't do the mission. The results over a 50 foot obstacle:

	Landing - ft.	Takeoff - ft.
C-130B	1710/clay; 1720/sand	1980/clay; 2150/sand
JC-130B	no data	no data; 1940/sand
NC-130B	1650/clay; 1650/sand	1440/clay; 1440/sand
YC-123H	1310/clay; 1400/sand	1760/clay; 1820/sand

For all aircraft except the NC-130 takeoffs were critical and all takeoffs were made at least 15 knots below minimum control speed. This US Army 20,000-lb blivet never did show up in the 32 months I spent flying trash in Vietnam so the whole program was probably chasing a ghost.

These test were tough on airframes, brakes, engines, etc. On the C-130s we averaged an engine change every four sand landings. We went through brakes; maintenance got expert at rebuilding them. Despite all the high-level concern on these tests, TAC, which owned the C-130 trash haulers, would only allow one sentence in the flight manual; to wit, "A C-130 can operate from a surface with a CBR of 3 to 5." TAC thought that the report should be classified "burn before reading." The test force felt that operation on unprepared surfaces should be reserved for extreme emergencies. One positive note, the Brigadier General in charge of in-country airlift during the Persian Gulf War did procure the C-130B data for possible use.

The tests did produce some interesting moments. The C-130B damaged the aft fuselage in a landing at Harpers Lake. I was appointed accident investigating officer. I doubt this was legal since I was not unbiased, but we got away with it. Another such moment occurred while I was riding co-pilot for Bill Loewe. He demonstrated the positive damping of the C-130 on a final approach at 92 KIAS with a stall speed of 89 KIAS. I admired his professional curiosity, but he scared me silly.

HERCULES STUCK IN THE MUD
by Rob Ransone Copyright (c) 1995 Ransone Associates, Inc.
Used by permission

In the fall of 1962, ASD and the AFFTC conducted a series of tests to determine the minimum field surface conditions on which assault transport operations could be performed. A follow-on to an earlier "Rough Road" test of the Lockheed C-130B and Fairchild JC-123B, this project was called "Rough Road Alpha," and included two C-123 and three C-130 aircraft. The C-123 fleet comprised a standard aircraft, and a modified aircraft on which CJ-610-1 turbojet engines were installed under each wing in addition to the two R2800-99W supercharged radial engines. The C-130 fleet comprised a standard C-130, a slightly modified C-130 with higher propeller speeds and larger flap deflections, and an NC-130B that was highly modified by addition of boundary layer control (BLC) blowing. Since I seemed to get the weird tests at Edwards, I got the BLC airplane.

NC-130B was a production C-130B, powered by four T56-A-7 turboprop engines, on which two strange looking jet engines had been hung under the outboard wing sections. They were strange looking because, although they had air inlets in the front for air to get in, they had no apparent holes in the back for the jet exhaust to get out! One might think the aircraft would puff up, sort of like a blimp! Not to worry. The jet exhaust was ducted up through the aircraft, and eventually came out over the flaps (which could be deflected to 90 degrees), the ailerons and elevators, and the rudder (with increased deflection and lengthened chord).

I first heard about this program one Friday night, just before dinner, when Ray Johnson, the Chief Project Engineer, telephoned me. He described

Lockheed NC-130B test aircraft stuck in the mud at Harper's dry lake.

the program, and asked if I would run the BLC tests.

"OK. When is the airplane coming to Edwards?"

"It just landed," Ray answered, smugly.

"Your first flight is in the morning at 0900."

"Thanks for the advance warning. Got anything for me to read to-night?"

Bright and early the next morning, I arrived at the airplane, met the pilot and copilot from ASD, and was accosted by the crew chief.

"How much tire pressure do you want?"

"55 psi." I answered, also smugly —thank you, Ray, for the Rough Road test reports last night!

Our first tests, airspeed calibrations, showed that the pitot-static system improvements had not kept up with the airplane aerodynamic improvements. C-130B assault landing approaches were normally flown at about 93 knots and touchdowns at about 87 knots. For the NC-130B BLC airplane, these speeds were reduced to about 70 and 65 knots, respectively. The problem, however, was that we really had no idea how fast we were flying. With 90 degrees of flaps, the airplane did not stall, but developed higher rates of sink. As we "decelerated" the indicated airspeed slowed to 55 knots, then 50 knots, and then started increasing to 55 knots, and then 60 knots, and the sink rate increased and pilot static errors increased. We believed that we were slowing down, but the airspeed indicator disagreed. On one 60-knot approach to the main runway, an F-104, cleared for landing behind us, finally called the tower:

"Tower! Isn't that airplane going awfully slow for a C-130?"

Ah, Eddie Tower. Would you send a big tow truck out to Harper's Lake? Our airplane is stuck in the mud.

The first assault field operations we tested were on soft clay at Harper's Dry Lake. The U.S. Army Corps of Engineers from the Waterways Experiment Station, Vicksburg, Mississippi, were supporting our tests by measuring the load bearing capability of the test fields. They used California Bearing Ratios (CBR), in which a rating of 100 is equivalent to crushed limestone. These engineers would measure areas of Harper's Lake, and we would land and take off at those areas, and note any problems.

The problem was, there weren't any problems! We should have been sinking into the soft clay, but we weren't. We theorized that the dry clay on the surface was being pressed into the damp clay underneath by the wide tires, and we were actually creating a workable runway surface as we went. On a Sunday morning, we were at Harper's Lake, taxiing our big NC-130B slowly around the lake bed, following the engineer as he walked along, sticking his probe into the soil to measure its CBR. An unusual sight, even for Edwards. All of a sudden, we got the data point we were after! The airplane just sort of leaned over to the left and stopped. Our left main land-

Lockheed NC-130B using reverse thrust during a landing in soft sand at Yuma, Arizona.

ing gear had sunk into the soft clay, rutting 22 inches deep. The left wing tip was at eye level.

We radioed Edwards. Were they glad to hear from us on a Sunday afternoon? Sure!

Why land on a hard old runway, when the sand is so nice and soft?

After two big bulldozers towed our airplane out of the mud at Harper's Lake, our next test area was in soft sand down at Yuma Naval Air Station, Arizona. The CBR of the sand test area, alongside the main runway, was zero. Zip. Nothing. The probe just went down into the sand with no resistance or reading at all. But taxi tests showed that the fat tires provided sufficient flotation for operations, even with these conditions. My main concern, however, was sand recirculation into the engines. With 90-degrees of flaps, and boundary layer air blowing over the wings and flaps, the sand would recirculate into the engine inlets during reverse thrust on landing roll out. This would not be good on the engine compressors, and the engines had no sand separators. Furthermore, our assault takeoffs were about 35 knots below the engine out control speed, and I didn't fancy flipping upside down right after takeoff. Neither did the rest of the crew. Therefore, I planned our tests to complete all of the assault takeoffs from the sand first, landing on the concrete runway; and then doing our assault landings in the sand, taking off at safe, higher speeds from the concrete runway. I got no arguments from the rest of the flight crew. We finished our takeoffs without incident.

The landings were spectacular. During landing rollout, with full flaps and reverse thrust, the entire aircraft was enveloped in a sand storm, with only the tip of the vertical tail and the wing tips sticking out of the cloud. On one landing, a Navy A4D had been cleared to land on the runway. Shortly after his clearance, tower cleared us to land in the opposite direction. This did not go unnoticed by the Navy pilot.

"Yuma tower! Did you just clear that Air Force one-thirty to land on the other end of my runway?"

"Affirmative. But he isn't going to land on the runway — he's going to land in the sand beside the runway." A moment of silence.

"Say again, tower. He's not going to land on the RUNWAY, he's going to land in the SAND beside the runway?"

"That's affirmative."

Navy took a waveoff—he didn't want any part of that crazy operation.

We finished our tests without further incident, loaded the ground crew and theodolite cameras on the airplane, and prepared to fly back to

Edwards. Takeoff position on the runway. Full power check. Ten seconds, OK. Then two "bangs" and number three engine quit cold. I have never heard a turboprop engine backfire, before or since. We tried again. Same result. The engine would not hold takeoff power, because the sand had eroded the compressor blades enough to cause a compressor stall and instantaneous power failure.

We flew back on another C-130, and left the NC-130B BLC at Yuma for an engine change. Good plan to do our assault takeoffs first.

ADRENALINE, RESPONSIBILITY AND HEART RATE
by Bob Hoey

The medical community became very interested and involved in the X-15 and Mercury programs from their inception. In fact the early AF version of the Mercury program (Man In Space Soonest, MISS) was generated by the AF Medical Laboratory. Their interest was, of course, the zero-g portion of each mission; about 2 minutes for the X-15 and for sub-orbital Mercury shots, but several hours for the orbital shots. Special instrumentation was devised to measure the heart rate, respiration rate and blood pressure of the pilot in flight. Prior to these flights the only high-stress medical measurements available to the medical community were athletes who were undergoing short duration, intense physical activity. Based on this data the MDs on the Mercury program had established a maximum heart rate limit which would be cause for a launch abort. The X-15 medical involvement was more "low key" since we planned to build up to the zero g flights in a more gradual fashion. During the captive phase of one of Scott Crossfield's flights, he called down to the flight surgeon who was monitoring the medical measurements in the control room, "How am I doing, Doc?" The flight surgeon's reply was that everything looked good. Scott came back with "Like hell! I've been holding my breath for over a minute."

On the early X-15 flights (completely normal flights) the MDs were surprised to observe heart rates peaking at 130 to 150 at launch and again during the landing, much higher than they had expected. These findings were transmitted to the Mercury medical folks causing them to raise their launch abort limits. If this information had not been available, Al Shepard's sub-orbital launch would surely have been aborted based on his high heart rate.

I was one of the flight planners during the early X-15 envelope expansion flights. The flight planners were intimately familiar with each individual flight and all of the potential emergency procedures, having devised them and flown them many times on the X-15 simulator. On the early flights we had little confidence in the inertial navigation system and found that the best parameter for determining the amount of energy imparted to the airplane (and thus the glide range potential if the engine quit) was engine burn time. We had installed a stop watch in the cockpit which was activated when the propellant valves opened and closed. As a backup, we manually started a stop watch in the control room when we saw the chamber pressure increase on the telemetry data. On one of Joe Walker's early flights my sole job in the control room was to start and stop that backup stop watch. There were some potential systems problems on the X-15 as the B-52 approached the launch point and it was obvious that this launch was going to be another "cliff-hanger". About 10 seconds before launch Joe called "abort, abort" and the entire team immediately switched to the abort checklist and began shutting down the systems. My job had just been deferred to another day and I was standing there with a stop watch in my hand so I took my own pulse. It was 130, only slightly below the value being measured on the X-15 pilot!

Subsequent measurements of heart rates for the X-15 ground controllers and pilots of remotely piloted vehicles, as well as other in-flight measurements, showed that high heart rate was apparently related mostly to anxiety and the sense of responsibility for what was taking place. The physical "g" environment had only a minor and predictable effect.

RIDING "THE WHEEL"
by Bob Hoey

One of the first attempts to truly simulate, in closed loop fashion, the g environment of an airplane was conducted at Johnsville, PA. in 1958 using a 6-degree-of-freedom analog simulator tied to a large centrifuge. The aircraft analog simulation produced three translational accelerations (in real time) which were converted into three centrifuge gimbal commands. The simulation cockpit was installed in the gondola and all cockpit signals were transferred to or from the gondola through slip rings at the center of rotation. The pilot could pulse the stick and watch the instruments respond while simultaneously feeling the appropriate g forces. (Although this really sounds great, the large and ERRONEOUS rotational accelerations required to properly align the linear accelerations on the gondola were a major distraction for dynamic maneuvers.) The airplane being simulated was the X-15 and the objective was to validate the crew station design including the restraint system, the side arm controller, and accessibility of various switches and controls. (Remember that the X-15 pilot was to experience over 4 g "eyeballs in" during

*Scott Crossfield preparing for a simulated X-15 entry on the
Navy's Johnsville Centrifuge.*

the powered phase, and later, 6 g "eyeballs down" simultaneously with 3 g "eyeballs out" during entry.) During thunderstorms we had to shut down since spikes in the analog computer would produce instantaneous 9 g transients at the gondola. The program was fairly successful resulting in several changes to the cockpit even though the pilots claimed that it was more like riding a trolley than flying an airplane. I was at Johnsville during most of the program and, although I flew several static runs from the gondola cockpit, I never rode "the wheel."

A similar program was conducted to validate the crew station for the X-20 Dyna Soar program in 1962. Only the boost phase was simulated and the g environment was not as severe. (between 2 and 6 g "eyeballs-in" for about 6 minutes). The piloting task was to fly the booster (Titan III) from lift-off to orbital insertion in all 3 axes using the booster autopilot. This turned out to be a trivial task of zeroing three guidance command needles, so we began to explore alternate guidance schemes and failure modes. The physiologists and psychologists had also devised several parallel experiments. In an effort to quantify pilot work load, a communication script was created and pilots were asked to call out various instrument readings throughout each run on the theory that the pilots would miss more calls when their work load was high. As the AFFTC on-site test engineer I flew many static runs during the program and finally talked my way into a ride on "the wheel". All of the X-20 pilots had been instrumented for heart rate, blood pressure, EKG, etc. As I began suiting up for the ride I asked the flight surgeon, Col Harry Bratt, why he hadn't instrumented me. He looked at me quizzically and said "you're a flight test engineer, aren't you?" When I said yes he responded, with a smile, "Well then, you're expendable."

The run I had chosen was of moderate difficulty including some wind shear and a damper failure on an upper stage. I had told myself that I would perform the run just like the pilots had been doing, including all instrument callouts for the psychologist. After strapping in and completing the preparation check list I said I was ready and "the wheel" started up. Although I experienced several seconds of vertigo following the first staging maneuver, I flew the booster right into orbit with no real difficulty. After shutdown I realized that I had not said a single word for the entire 6-minute run! Furthermore, no one in the control room had even asked me how I was doing! I never did ask the psychologist what conclusion he reached from that run, although he probably would have concluded that I had been "expended."

§

President Kennedy was assassinated in Dallas Texas.

The X-15 continued to reach higher into space. It was capable of reaching an altitude of nearly 500,000 feet, but was not designed to complete a reentry from this altitude. Both the airplane and the pilot's limitations would have been exceeded if such a reentry had been attempted. In 1963 Joe Walker reached the maximum practical altitude for the X-15 of 354,200 feet.

A few miles to the north of Edwards, the A-12 also quietly reached its design goal of a sustained cruise at 3.2 times the speed of sound, and operational flights soon began.

Early in 1963 the light-weight M2-F1 Lifting Body (commonly referred to as the "flying bathtub") began car tows on Rogers Lakebed at DFRC with Milt Thompson at the controls. Later in the year it began air tows behind a C-47 "Gooney Bird."

THE BEGINNING OF THE LIFTING BODY PROGRAM
by Frank Anderton

When the X-20 DYNA SOAR was cancelled in 1963, I was reassigned as the AFFTC X-15 Liaison Officer. I was a rated Captain and with this new job came considerable ribbing that my main function was to chase the cows off the emergency landing dry lakes before launch, and there was some truth in that. It was through this new job that I became involved with the Lifting Body Program.

These were interesting days at Edwards. There were many highly advanced aircraft in test at the center in the early years of the 60s including the XB-70 and SR-71. The X-15 joint NASA FRC/AFFTC flight test program was very successful; new speed and altitude records were being set with almost every flight and reams of data were being gathered. Engineers at FRC and AFFTC were working on exotic concepts for air launching orbital vehicles. (These concepts remained dormant until the recent successful flights of the Pegasus vehicle.) There was a real sense of excitement in the air as it seemed that something new was happening every day.

One of the hottest subjects of debate was the best aerodynamic shape for lifting reentry vehicles. There were design proposals from NASA Langley (HL-10) and NASA Ames (M2) and later from the Air Force (SV-5).

169

The "heavy weight" lifting bodies. L to r: Air Force/Martin X-24A, NASA/ Northrop M2-F3, NASA/Northrop HL-10.

The principle goal of these designs was a shape that could withstand reentry heating. This difficult requirement led to some unusual configurations which were expected to have daunting transonic and low speed stability and control problems. Some early work with a wooden glider, (M2-F1), built under the direction of Dale Reed at NASA FRC, had confirmed that potentially solvable problems existed. Plans were laid to build full-up test aircraft of the M2 and HL-10 which would explore the transonic and supersonic regime. Later an Air Force SV-5 shape (redesignated the X-24A) was built.

A formal agreement between the AFFTC and NASA FRC for testing the new aircraft was needed. I drafted up a joint testing agreement based on the X-15 agreement, and we began preparations to brief this agreement and program requirements to headquarters AFSC (ARDC). A unique requirement of this program was the need to overhaul the old XLR-11 rocket engines, many of which had been lying dormant since the X-1 program. The engines needed to be rebuilt and drawings were needed so that we could maintain them. John McTigue of FRC was very familiar with the location and status of the engines. We contacted Reaction Motors Inc. (RMI) for a quote on funding needed to do the job, and with the concurrence of Gen. Branch and Paul Bikle, I put together a short briefing to take to Air Force Systems Command to obtain the needed funds.

Everything was ready to take to Washington. The viewgraphs had been made and the briefing approved by all levels. At the last moment, we received a new bid from RMI. We felt that the new (and higher) costs were not justified, but it was too late to negotiate with RMI. We didn't even have time to change the viewgraphs, we had an appointment to keep in Washington. It was a frustrating situation, since it looked like we didn't know what we were doing when actually we had a really good handle on the problem. It unfairly put Gen. Branch on the spot.

We flew to Andrews in an AFFTC T-39, and spent the night in the VOQ. Gen Branch insisted that I stay in VIP quarters with him and told me to "wing a shoe at me if I snore." We briefed the Vice Commander of AFSC (ARDC) the following morning and everything went great. The cost increase was embarrassing to the general, but it was not big bucks so we got our approval.

Upon returning to the Center, we reorganized the engine rebuild program by doing some of the tasks in-house and contracting the remainder on a piece-by-piece basis, resulting in an overall cost lower than the original estimate. Thus began one of the most frugal, yet most productive research flight test programs ever conducted by the government.

THE NF-104A FLAT SPIN
by Bob Hoey

Since I was the first AF flight test engineer to do stability and control flight testing of the F-104A, I had become sort of the local expert on the F-104. I had moved to a supervisory position in the Flight Research Branch where I was trying to infuse the use of simulation into other ongoing test programs.

The Test Pilot School (TPS) had contracted with Lockheed to modify three F-104As to add AR-121-NA-1 rocket engines, and to equip the aircraft with reaction control systems similar to those used in the X-15. The intent was to zoom the airplanes to about 100,000 feet altitude and train future space pilots on the peculiarities of high altitude flight. After a few system checkout flights by Lockheed, the first NF-104 was delivered to Edwards in October of 1963. Col. Guy Townsend, the Test Wing Commander, decided that the airplane should undergo a developmental test program under the cognizance of Flight Test Engineering and Test Operations before being turned over to the Test Pilot School. Clen Hendrickson was assigned as Project Engineer, and Major Bob Smith was assigned as Test Pilot. I saw this as a perfect opportunity to apply simulation technology to support a challenging flight test program and we programmed a 3 degree-of-freedom and a 5 degree-of-freedom simulation of the airplane. By December of 1963 both simulations were operating and we were in the process of validating various features, and using them in the flight planning process for the primary test airplane. The other two airplanes were delivered to the Test Pilot School in December and the instructors began familiarizing themselves with the NF-104A's characteristics.

In late December 1963 (about the time of the X-20 cancellation) Col. Yeager, who was the Commandant of the TPS, ejected from one of the NF-104s following an attempt to set a new altitude record. I was assigned to assist the accident board which was headed by the Wing Commander, Col Guy Townsend.

My recollection is that Col. Yeager had not flown either of our two simulations prior to this flight, however, the analog computers of that day were pretty temperamental and the concept of using simulation to support flight testing was still in its infancy.

Col. Yeager's zoom started at a lower energy level than desired due to warm atmospheric temperatures. As the aircraft reached maximum altitude (about 101,000 feet) the angle of attack increased rather abruptly and the aircraft entered a highly oscillatory spin (typical for an F-104, and usually recoverable). After three oscillatory turns to the right, it reversed direction, the angle of attack stabilized at a very high value, the oscillations subsided, and the airplane began a stable flat spin to the left (NOT typical for an F-104). Spin recovery controls were applied several times but the flat spin continued. At about 17,000 feet the drag chute was deployed. The aircraft recovered and entered a vertical dive. While the speed was increasing in the dive, the drag chute was released and the aircraft abruptly pitched up and re-entered the flat spin. Shortly after this, at about 7000 feet, Col Yeager ejected. After separating from the ejection seat, the rocket motor on the seat impacted his helmet, breaking the faceplate and igniting the rubber face seal. He scraped the burning rubber out of his helmet with his gloved hand but received severe burns to his face and hands in the process.

Although the aircraft was still in a flat spin at impact, nearly all of the test data were recovered. The on-board data, coupled with the radar data, audio tapes and Askania cameras, allowed the details of the flight to be completely reconstructed within two weeks of the accident. Col. Yeager was in the Edwards AFB hospital recovering from severe burns and was not available for interview. As soon as he was able, he met with the accident board to give his account of the flight. The result was an amazing demonstration of a disciplined test pilot with total recall! Col Yeager recounted every event on the flight in complete detail, including the number of oscillatory spins before it changed direction and went "flat", and various gage readings throughout the flight. The only data point that he missed, as I remember, was the altitude at which he had deployed the drag chute.

The next step was to determine why the airplane behaved the way it did and what could be done to prevent similar events in the future. In order to reach maximum altitude, a very high pitch angle was required during the climb (about 50 degrees). At the peak of the climb there was a very rapid change in flight path angle as the steep climb angle changed to a steep descent angle. A fairly rapid nose-down pitch rotation was required by the

Lockheed NF-104 during steep zoom climb.

pilot at peak altitude in order to keep the nose of the aircraft pointed into the wind. The only indication to the pilot that peak altitude had been reached was the rapid increase in angle of attack as the flight path changed from ascent to descent. Col. Yeager had delayed the start of this nose-down rotation momentarily since the rocket engine was still burning. When he did initiate the pitch-down rotation, the angle of attack had already passed into a region of pitch instability and neither his application of nose-down stabilizer nor nose-down pitch reaction controls were sufficient to realign the aircraft with the flight path.

We immediately went to the two NF-104 simulations to attempt to duplicate the conditions near the top of the zoom on Yeager's flight. It easily duplicated the entry into the deep stall condition, including the inability of the aerodynamic and reaction controls to affect a recovery. The simulation was also used to duplicate the recovery from the deep stall using the drag chute, and to further duplicate the subsequent pitchup and return to the deep stall.

This was the first time that an F-104 had experienced a deep stall and flat spin, although a deep stall condition had been observed in the Langley Spin Tunnels early in the F-104's development. In June of 1964 a standard F-104A, being flown by a student at the TPS, was performing a zoom climb to about 80,000 feet. He also encountered a deep stall and flat spin. The aircraft failed to recover, but the pilot ejected successfully. When we heard the pilot's description of the departure as a large yaw associated with his application of forward stick, the ol' light bulb clicked on! We returned to the simulator and added engine gyroscopic terms to the equations. Sure enough, we found that the gyroscopic effects were very significant when the dynamic pressure was below about 20 pounds per square foot. Further study revealed that the engine gyroscopic effects were probably the primary contributing factor to the oscillatory nature of the normal F-104 spin. On zoom missions the afterburner and engine were shut down during the ascent to prevent engine overtemp. The RPM was thus slowing throughout the remainder of the zoom until a relight was attempted at lower altitude. Engine RPM at peak altitude was sufficient to cause the initial departures to be oscillatory, but the decreasing gyroscopic effect as the engine slowed, allowed both airplanes to stabilize in a deep stall.

§

The Strategic Air Command, concerned about the increasing vulnerability of its B-52 fleet, contracted with North American to build a prototype high altitude, bomber that would cruise at 3 times the speed of sound. The XB-70A "Valkyrie" made its maiden flight in 1964, flown by North American's Al White and Air Force Col. Joe Cotton. The Air Force had also decided to buy a slightly modified, 2-seat version of Lockheed's highly successful A-12, the SR-71 "Blackbird" which also flew for the first time in 1964. The XB-70A was a controversial aircraft from the outset, while the very existence of the A-12's and SR-71's remained under tight secrecy.

The Lockheed C-141A "Starlifter", the first all-jet airlifter, arrived at Edwards for testing.

The F-111 "swing wing" aircraft made its first flight. There will be very few new AF aircraft models until the A-9/A-10 fly-offs in 1972.

The AFFTC Mission Control Rooms (MCRs) to support XB-70 testing were made operational. The MCRs included telemetry displays, space positioning information, and communications equipment.

During another visit to Edwards, Jackie Cochran became the first woman to reach Mach 2 flying an F-104G.

B-58 LOW ALTITUDE PERFORMANCE
by Jerry Jones

In the fall of 1963, shortly after I arrived at Edwards AFB, I was assigned to work as a flight test engineer on the B-58 Multi-weapons Performance, Stability and Control Program. The Project Engineer was Dick Abrams and the Project Pilot was Maj. Charlie Bock.

I was a young engineer right out of college, so my assignment for the first few months I was on the program was to supervise the efforts of a couple of engineering technicians who were hand-tabulating data from photo-panel film to paper spreadsheets. This data was then transferred by hand to computer punch cards and processed through performance analysis programs on an IBM 1620 computer which had less compute capacity than most hand-held computers do these days. My experience with the actual aircraft was limited to walking around it and looking in the cockpit when it was on the ground and watching it take off and land during a couple of test missions. It

General Dynamics' B-58 "Hustler."

was a mighty impressive sight!

Then one day in early spring 1964, Dick came to me and said, "Jerry, I think its time you got some experience flying in the aircraft and running a test mission." My heart leaped out of my chest and I nearly fainted on the spot! He said, "But, you've got to get an altitude chamber indoctrination and a flight physical and do a lot of OJT on how to prepare for a test mission and how to operate the test instrumentation in the aircraft." After recovering my composure, I said OK and went about the task of studying and preparing for my first flight. This was not only going to be my first flight in the B-58, but, my very first flight in an Air Force airplane, period. I had just begun taking private pilot's lessons in a Cessna 150 at Fox Field in Lancaster and was auditing TPS classes for the academics, but, this was something entirely different.

The mission that I was planning to fly was a cruise performance mission, so it was not supposed to be a very aggressive flight — just straight and level for the most part. What Dick did not tell me ahead of time was that the last test to be put on the test card was a low altitude speed-power at a weight-pressure ratio of 140K. Those of you who do not know about the B-58 need to know that the usual landing weight of this delta-wing bomber aircraft was about 80,000 pounds. The three crew stations in the aircraft were very spartan and separated. Only the pilot had a real good view outside with the second and third stations being equipped with a small porthole on each side to look out of. Since this was to be a low-level test, we planned to do it out over the Pacific Ocean and allow enough fuel to return to Edwards and land. Figuring that the test would consume from 30-40,000 pounds of fuel and allowing another 10-15,000 pounds for the return to base, meant that the test was to be commenced at a gross weight of 130-140,000 pounds. This meant that the test would start at an altitude below 2,000 feet and climb as fuel was burned off.

On the day of the mission, everything was going well. The weather was clear, the mission was proceeding on schedule, and I was beginning to feel comfortable with the airplane and my routine. As the time approached to descend and conduct the low altitude test, I discussed with the pilot that we would accelerate as we descended and get the high speed point first. Our normal procedure was to estimate the actual gross weight that we would be at when we arrived on conditions, and then calculate the altitude to fly at based upon that weight. During our descent, I was busily calculating the test altitude and as a final step, subtracting out the pitot-static error so that I could give the pilot an indicated altitude at which to level off. Since our gross weight was just under 140,000 pounds, I knew the altitude was going to be low, but what I calculated shocked me! Not wanting to be caught in a foolish mistake, I did the calculations again. I got the same answer! I announced to the pilot, "Charlie, my calculations show that the first test point is at an indicated altitude of minus 300 feet, but..." Major Bock broke in with a chuckle and said, "Yes, Jerry, I'll be sure to watch outside and not fly below sea level!" Once we got that little item cleared up, everything else was great and I really enjoyed watching the sailboats as we skimmed along a couple of hundred feet above the water. The boats must have had a good show too!

SOMETIMES IT'S JUST NOT YOUR TIME
by Bill Schweikhard

Late in 1964 the Northrop T-38 Talon test program was coming to a close. The USAF Test Pilot School was in need of a more modern trainer having supersonic capability. The Test Pilot School was a good place for the cast-offs of the T-38 test force to find a home. Otherwise, their being nonstandard, they would probably be sent to the bone yard at Davis-Monthan AFB, Arizona. The school was beginning to qualify its instructors to fly the airplane. One afternoon Tom Stafford announced that he had a back seat open and would I like to take a look at the airplane from an engineer's point of view and how we might use it in the curriculum. It took me about three seconds to say yes — grabbed my parachute and helmet, and we were off.

177

The flight was uneventful as we put it through the paces. Tom convinced me that it was easy to fly and a very docile airplane. That was the case until we came into the traffic pattern.

We came in from the west and did a traditional 360 overhead approach beginning with a 3-g break from 1,000 above the runway to a downwind where the gear and flaps were lowered. As we straightened out on a westerly heading there was a loud bang and a violent roll to the right. We were inverted in less than one second where Tom had stopped the roll with us

Northrop T-38 "Talon" on initial approach with Test Pilot School in background.

looking up at the desert. I grabbed for the ejection handles in anticipation of the airplane rolling upright. Had it happened Tom would have been talking to himself. I thought that we were in a mid-air collision and as Tom was slowly getting the airplane back to an upright condition I was looking for the other airplane. I could see nothing but as I looked back I could only see a couple of inches of the flap on each side. The right one was up; the left one was down. I informed Tom of this situation as he was muttering "We're in deep shit" over and over again. He snapped back, "What am I supposed to do about it? I've got full rudder and full aileron in and it's taking all of the strength I've got." So I put up the flaps and gear from the back seat and he pushed up the throttle to arrest our descent. By this time we were less than 200 feet above the ground and about to go for a swim in Pancho Barnes' now abandoned swimming pool. The single flap that was down came up smoothly.

Tom collected himself and in a very professional manner and with a gift for understatement called: "Eddie Tower we're breaking out of traffic, we have a little problem here." If anyone in the tower was looking I wonder what they were thinking. If they were, they didn't let on and came back with a businesslike "Roger." We continued to the west as we climbed back to the traffic pattern altitude and Tom said that we could make a no-flap landing, "no sweat." I thought for a few seconds as I looked back at the left flap that was in the normal position and the right flap whose trailing edge was above that of the wing. I asked Tom what was going to happen to that free flap when we slowed down. He said, "I don't know"; and neither did I. I said, why don't we go out over the lake bed and do a 1-g stall approach at altitude. It took about a millisecond for him to agree. So he called the tower to announce our problem and our intentions. We both agreed that one uncontrolled roll near the ground was enough for one day. The flap stayed up, so we did a no-flap landing without further incident. But there were two very pale people who got out of that airplane that calm Edwards afternoon. We were anything but calm.

Later that week Jay Hanks went up with an airplane that had been modified to allow only one flap to be actuated and did tests at altitude that indicated that the airplane was not recoverable had we been flying five knots slower. IT JUST WASN'T OUR TIME.

Moral: Docile airplane can sometimes be anything but. Be prepared. Never let your guard down and live to tell about it.

§

By 1965 the XB-70A had reached its design cruise Mach number of 3.0. The Air Force had decided not to pursue production of the big bomber, however, opting instead to upgrade the B-52 fleet to perform low altitude penetration flights. The two B-70's were turned over to an AF/ NASA joint test team for further research into the supersonic cruise environment.

The United States deployed its first combat troops to Vietnam which rapidly became another testing ground for modern weaponry.

C-133 WITCH HUNT
by Jerry Jones

For many years prior to the C-5A, the C-133 was the largest cargo aircraft ever introduced into the Air Force inventory. In the fall of 1964, I was assigned as project engineer to the C-133 Phase II Stability and Control Reevaluation Program. The project pilot was Maj. Doug Benefield and my branch supervisor was Charlie Johnson. The C-133 had been a workhorse of the fleet during the late 50s and early 60s, since it was the only aircraft in the inventory that could carry out-sized (large volume) cargo. Due to the cold war situation during that time, the C-133 mission was a high priority to the Air Force.

A number of very mysterious accidents had begun to plague the C-133s resulting in seven aircraft being lost and all crew members killed. The airplane was getting such a bad reputation that the operational pilots were becoming spooky about flying it and the Air Force decided to ground the aircraft until a cause, or causes, could be identified for the accidents. Douglas Aircraft in Long Beach was contracted to instrument an airplane and the AFFTC was tasked to begin an investigation of possible causes for the accidents. There were quite a number of possible causes proposed and we were directed to perform tests to verify which of a representative number of these causes were plausible.

One of the causes that showed the most promise as a plausible explanation for the majority of the accidents was that the airplane could have decelerated into an aerodynamic stall while low to the ground and had insufficient altitude for recovery. Obviously, we could not demonstrate this by performing stall tests at low altitude, but, we decided that stall tests at an altitude of 10,000 feet was safe and would be sufficient to prove our hypoth-

Douglas C-133.

esis. Since the C-133 was a four-engine, turboprop-powered aircraft, power effects due to propwash over the wing was also a factor that had to be investigated. This stall testing subsequently would yield the most significant findings of our entire test program and consumed considerably more time and resources than we had bargained for.

The entire upper surface of the left and right wings on the test aircraft were tufted and cameras were installed in the vertical tail and wing center section to film tuft activity. Crew accommodations in the C-133 consisted of a four-crew cockpit for the pilot, copilot, flight engineer, and navigator. As flight test engineer, my work station in the test aircraft was a photo panel and oscillograph control panel installed in the crew rest area behind the main flight deck. My only view to the outside was a small porthole, approximately six inches in diameter, to the left and right of my seat, which faced forward.

All test results demonstrated on the first five flights of the test program were essentially the same as reported in the original test reports written in 1960. The stability and control characteristics within the operational envelope were unchanged and relatively benign. The first stall tests were conducted on the sixth flight and were "the same as those experienced on previous C-133 stall tests." A correct statement in print, but, nonetheless frightening to a young engineer who had never experienced "out of control flight" before.

The typical stall characteristics for the day were: little or no aerodynamic stall warning, an abrupt right rolloff with yawing motion of the nose to the left and severe airframe buffet at the stall! In addition, there was little or no response to aileron control inputs while in the stall; a disconcerting fact as the aircraft snap-rolls to the right!

As was his custom, Charlie Johnson met us at the aircraft after the flight to see how things went. I walked up to him and said something like, "Charlie, what did I do to deserve this?" He looked at me and said, "What do you mean , Jerry?" I said "I don't think airplanes this size were meant to fly upside down!" Charlie smiled at me and Doug Benefield, who was standing behind me and said, "Welcome to flight test, Jerry!" This was an inauspicious beginning to a test program that would eventually total up to more than 500 stalls and lead to the development of a 12-inch stall strip which we carefully located on the leading edge of the left wing of the aircraft to induce stall to occur on both wings at the same time and significantly reduce the rolling tendency of the aircraft.

As is the case in most of these stories, this was not the end, however. The System Program Office then requested that we "demonstrate" our fix on selected aircraft in the operational fleet and to take operational pilots with us on the flights in order to help renew their confidence in the aircraft. So, with a template cut from a sheet of 1/4-inch plywood to locate a stall strip on the leading edge of the wing and a roll of Mach-tape with which to attach it, Maj. Benefield, our flight engineer and I started our road show! Our routine was; (1) travel to either Dover AFB, Delaware or Travis AFB, California and select an aircraft that was available for the demonstration, (2) take a preselected and somewhat apprehensive operational pilot and go for a short flight to demonstrate the unmodified stall characteristics, (3) install the stall strip, and (4) refly the same stalls on a second flight and show them (and ourselves) that our fix improved the stall characteristics. We felt like carnival barkers and often drew crowds as I climbed up on a maintenance stand and installed the stall strip with my trusty template and Mach tape. All went well until —"the Dover Dog."

The "Dover Dog" was an airplane that had gotten a bad reputation at Dover AFB for "not flying right." None of the operational pilots wanted to fly the aircraft because it didn't fly like the rest of the airplanes and strange things happened when they flew it! So we took it for a spin. A bad word to use — because, when we entered the first stall, the aircraft snap-rolled to the left! Son of a gun! We repeated a few more stalls to make sure it wasn't a random occurrence; sure enough, it consistently broke left. The operational pilot's eyes were big as saucers! When we got on the ground and it came time to install the stall strip, I looked at Doug and the crew chief and shrugged my shoulders; "Put the stand over by the right wing at the same place," I said. We installed the strip and climbed on the aircraft to fly. Just like we knew what we were doing, the stalls were very nice, very docile! We gained a lot of respect that day! The SPO, however, rewarded our resourcefulness by directing us to extend our demonstrations to every C-133 aircraft in the fleet to make sure there were no more dogs! Luckily, there were only 42 aircraft, and not a fleet the size of our current F-16 fleet!

X-19 A PRETTY AIRPLANE WITH UGLY HABITS
By Rob Ransone Copyright (c) 1995 Ransone Associates, Inc.
Used by permission

In 1959, Hank Borst developed a unique propeller VSTOL concept for Curtiss-Wright, that resulted in successful flight tests of the model X-100. This aircraft was a small, open cockpit demonstrator, with a short stubby wing and a turboprop exhaust exiting the tail to which diverter vanes had been installed for pitch control in hover. The propellers were most unusual. Normally propellers are narrow at the root, and may be wider at the tips. This is to minimize the "radial force" component of thrust that exists when any propeller's shaft is operating at a positive angle of attack to the airstream. This force acts in a vertical direction, in the propeller's plane of rotation. In other words, it provides lift. Hank reasoned that if a propeller was designed to maximize this radial force, a substantial lift vector could be realized, and the wing for a VSTOL aircraft could be made much smaller for improved cruise efficiency. The X-100 flight tests substantiated this concept, and Curtiss-Wright had Hank design a small VSTOL aircraft, the size and appearance of an Aero Commander, which was a popular twin engine executive transport of the day. They called it the Model 200.

With the advent of the Tri-Service VSTOL program, in 1962 Curtiss-Wright offered the government an essentially off-the-shelf vehicle for government tests. The government was interested, and paid Curtiss-Wright money to install, among other things, ejection seats and two GFE Lycoming T-55-L-5 free-turbine engines, and to rename the aircraft the X-19.

The ejection seats, located side-by-side in the small cockpit, are crucial to this story, as you shall see. They were the North American Aviation, LW-2B, which were capable of safe crew ejection from 0 to 500 knots, and 0 to 50,000 feet height. The design features that provided this remarkable capability were that the pilots stayed in the seat, to which the parachute was attached, and the parachute was inflated by a ballistic charge immediately upon ejection.

The X-19 was the prettiest little VSTOL aircraft of that era. The fuselage was the size and shape of an Aero Commander. It had tandem wings with four propellers, one at each wingtip, and twin engines in the aft fuselage. Cross-shafts from the two engines drove the four propellers, which could be tilted vertically for VTOL and hover, and rotated down for cruise flight. In hover, differential pitch between the forward and rear props provided longitudinal control, differential pitch between the port and starboard props provided lateral control, and differential pitch diagonally provided yaw

Curtiss-Wright X-19.

control — sort of.

Curtiss-Wright was to fly the initial Category I hover tests at its plant in Caldwell, New Jersey, then ship the X-19 to Edwards for its Category I STOL, conversion, and conventional tests. The Tri-Service VSTOL Test Force would then take over and fly the Category II and III tests at Edwards.

The first flight, a hover test at Caldwell, consisted of getting very light on the landing gear and rolling over, collapsing the right main gear. Subsequent attempts demonstrated terrible control harmony about the lateral and pitch axes, and the pilot's inability to handle the aircraft. No reflection on the pilot, who had been flying Curtiss-Wright's old B-17 with an extra engine in the nose for testing propellers — the X-19 was a real handful. The X-100 test pilot decided he wanted more money to fly the X-19 than Curtiss-Wright was willing to pay, so they finally hired a helicopter test pilot as chief test pilot. Realizing that the aircraft also had a non-helicopter flight mode, they hired a fixed-wing test pilot, who took a leave-of-absence from the FAA's NAFEC flight test facility in Atlantic City, New Jersey. In the mean time, back at Edwards, we were busily planning how we would conduct the Category II and III tests when the X-19 arrived.

Then, trouble: At a flight program planning meeting at the SPO, Curtiss-Wright proposed to conduct its Category I STOL and conventional tests at Caldwell, and said they could save the SPO over $100,000 (big money, in those days!) by not having to maintain the aircraft at Edwards.

The SPO loved this idea, but I objected—strongly. "There is no place to make an emergency landing on the East coast. With the dry lake bed at Edwards, we could land the aircraft almost anywhere." "The X-19 is not really a VSTOL aircraft," Curtiss-Wright countered, "it is a VTOL aircraft. In an emergency, it will reconvert to hover mode and land vertically. It can land vertically in a vacant lot." "I cannot imagine your completing Category I without a hydraulic failure or a gearbox problem," I argued. "In that case, I don't think the pilots will want to enter a more dangerous flight mode. I think they will elect to eject. That will be the end of the airplane, and the end of the X-19 program."

This time, I was overruled. The X-19 stayed on the East coast for Category I, but at least it was moved from Caldwell to NAFEC. The aircraft was designed to fly on only one engine — the two engines were only to provide engine out safety. In fact, to save weight, the transmissions and gearboxes were not designed to take the full power of both engines, and such power was prohibited by the flight manual. The flight manual also advised what to do in case of a total engine failure. "Put the aircraft into a dive, arrest your sink rate over the end of the runway, and touch down at 160 knots."

The flight manual then added, almost as an afterthought: "...but since the landing gear structural limit is only 65 knots, you're not going to make it, anyway, so just bail out if the engines quit." So much for emergency STOL landings.

I returned to Edwards, and told my flight test engineers to forget planning for Category II at Edwards. Get ready to monitor the Category I tests at NAFEC. I felt so strongly about this, that I entered into my journal the conviction that the X-19 was going to experience a hydraulic or gearbox failure at NAFEC, the pilots would bail out, the aircraft would crash, and the program would be canceled.

Normally, I would have had my engineers at Edwards preparing for the forthcoming Category II Performance and Stability and Control tests. In this case, however, I was so certain that the X-19 would never get to Edwards, and that if we were to get any information at all, we would have to get it during Curtiss-Wright's Category I tests. Therefore, I put our Category II preparations on hold, and sent my engineers to Caldwell, New Jersey.

Good move!

Although Bob Baldwin, our project test pilot, made one or two hover flights, the entire flight test program of 50 flights for a total of 3 hours and 51 minutes (think about that, for a moment) was flown by the contractor crew. The contractor pilot and copilot flew the first conversion flight at NAFEC on August 25, 1965. The X-19 was to make a STOL takeoff from the NAFEC main runway, climb to 500 feet, circle the field at airspeeds of 40 to 150 knots, and return to land on the main runway. Bob Baldwin, Don Wray (the Army test pilot), and Dick Homuth (the Navy test pilot) would chase in an H-34 helicopter, and the NAFEC ground cameras would track the entire flight.

Takeoff and climbout were normal. On the downwind leg, however, the copilot reported a high left rear nacelle gearbox temperature. The pilot thought he was reporting hydraulic pressure, and said "OK." At the turn to base leg, the copilot repeated his warning, and the pilot, this time, understood that they had a serious gearbox overtemp problem. He continued his turn, but, instead of lining up with the runway for an immediate landing, he headed for a small clearing in the trees. He was the helicopter pilot, remember, and had virtually no fixed wing experience.

The X-19 disappeared behind the trees, and the NAFEC camera operator, in the tower, asked Bob Reschak, my flight test project engineer, whether he should stop filming.

"Don't stop," Bob ordered. "Keep the cameras going."

Immediately, the X-19 came booming up from behind the trees. The copilot didn't know about landing helicopters, but he knew that any kind of landing in the trees at 105 knots was a bad plan, so he shoved the throttles forward. Remember that the transmission system was not designed for full power from both engines? At 390 feet above the ground, the left rear nacelle and prop broke loose, and the X-19 instantly pitched up and rolled left. Now the two engines were driving only three props, which also left the aircraft. Now two engines were running full power with nothing to run, so they oversped and exploded. It had been three seconds since the first prop had broken off, the X-19 was inverted and rolling at 180 degrees per second, and both pilot and copilot ejected towards the ground. One half second after ejection, the canopy thrusters fired, and 1.4 seconds later the chutes were fully deployed — still 230 feet above the ground. Both crew landed safely, with probably the only ejection system of the time that could have saved them.

The X-19 continued its rolling plunge and exploded upon impact. Curtiss-Wright did not know that rolls of oscillograph paper are hard to burn — they char on the outside, but frequently the inside can still be developed.

Fortunately, Bob Reschak was on hand to advise them, and the data were subsequently recovered. The X-19 never came to Edwards. The SPO canceled the X-19 program. I marked the price on my copy of our X-19 Category I Limited Flight Evaluation — $ 60,000 per copy.

WHEN SHE GETS UPRIGHT, GET OUT!
by Wen Painter

In the fall of 1965, after the rollout of the M2-F2, and the assignment of USAF Lifting Body Project Pilot, Capt. Jerauld "Jerry" R. Gentry, it was decided that he (Jerry) should be checked out in the M2-F1, the NASA lightweight lifting body.

The appropriate preparations were made for Jerry to fly the M2-F1 Lifting Body. He was sent up to Tehachapi, California, close to Edwards AFB, to fly gliders as well as attend briefings. The day came when Jerry made his first flight behind the NASA C-47 (Navy R4D) and Vic Horton was watching out of the dome (used to shoot the stars or sun for navigation) of the airplane and saw the M2-F1, with Jerry flying it, in a severe roll oscillation eventually rolling inverted. Vic called "When she gets upright, get out!" The launch crew in the C-47 did not know if the lifting body had crashed into the lakebed, or what had happened. The M2-F1 had been released by Jerry and had made a successful landing (with several broken structural components).

The first Lifting Body: the lightweight M2-F1.

This expression "WHEN SHE GETS UPRIGHT, GET OUT" then became a phrase used often after that. The M2-F1 was flown about a year later with Jerry at the controls and the same thing happened again, but this time Jerry released and fired the "INSTANT L/D" rockets and made a very good landing with no damage to the vehicle. This was the last flight of the M2-F1. It had made over 300 flights and it was decided by Paul Bikle, the NASA FRC Director, to retire the first Lifting Body.

LONGITUDINAL SHORT-PERIOD TESTING
by Hank Klung

In 1964, I came to Edwards from the F-105 System Program Office where one of my tasks had been to participate in a study of the possibility of PIO (pilot induced oscillations) in the F-105. At the time, this was a hot topic for new fighter type aircraft.

My second project at Edwards was to plan and conduct the Category II Stability and Control flight test of the F-5A. Previously, testing had been conducted by John Mitchell on the YF-5A (one of the N-156's modified to the F-5A configuration). My test was to determine the differences, if any, between the two models and to gather data to 100% loads.

The then-current method of determining longitudinal short-period characteristics in flight was for the pilot to use a rapid longitudinal stick pulse. Post-flight analysis of the resulting aircraft response would yield the desired parameters. The problem with this technique was that the damping ratios were usually high and the resulting aircraft motion did not lend itself to precise frequency and damping ratio determinations.

After discussion with Wally Nelson of Northrop, I decided to try using a frequency response method of testing. I used an audio tone fed into the pilot's headset as the cue. The frequency of the tone was varied at a sinusoidal rate. A span of rates was used with the span including the predicted natural frequency of the aircraft. The pilot then moved the control stick in time with the "music." Maj. Mike Adams and Maj. Pete Knight flew the preponderance of the test points. The data turned out great. The traces indicated an almost constant peak-to-peak amplitude of g's and stick displacement. I was amazed that the pilots could maintain this even when the stick displacement (and stabilator displacement) and normal force were about 180 degrees out of synch.

The people at Wright-Patterson were happy with the results; they sent a complimentary letter on the report back to us. Several years later I learned that our report had been included in the report substantiating the new

Northrop F-5A "Freedom Fighter."

MIL-F-8785 specification for aircraft flying qualities.

One drawback of this test method is the quantity of test time per test point. I learned a second drawback while flying in the back seat of a T-38 piloted by Tom Bell, who was an instructor in the test pilot school. Both Tom and I rapidly concluded that this maneuver is tough to take if you're not the one doing the stick shaking. The technique is not recommended with multiple persons on board unless there are a lot of accessible barf bags!

F-5A ROLL TEST
by Hank Klung

During supplemental Category II flying qualities testing of the Northrop F-5A during July and August of 1965, we planned a test to observe the aircraft's rolling characteristics with an asymmetric store loading. I do not remember the exact loading, but it involved a heavy store on one wing with the opposite wing clean. The appropriate contractor Category I testing had been completed, and our planned test conditions (relatively high subsonic speed and rapid, maximum stick deflection) were within the published flight manual limitations.

When I discussed the flight test card with Mike Adams, the pilot for the test, I had planned the roll to be away from the heavy wing. Mike suggested that the more interesting response should be obtained rolling into the heavy wing; on that, we agreed.

John Ludwig was flying the T-38 chase aircraft with me in the rear seat. We were to Mike's right rear. While the test aircraft was in straight and level flight as Mike was setting up for the test, I was surprised to see the amount of aileron input that was needed to hold the wings level and counterbalance the asymmetry, As Mike executed the roll, his aircraft experienced a very significant yaw, large enough that his hand was thrown off the throttle control. To us in the chase, the aircraft appeared to have temporarily gone out of control. John suspected that the aircraft might have experienced some damage, but our perusal from the chase disclosed none.

We immediately returned to Edwards. Further examination of the aircraft on the ground indicated that it had suffered no structural ill effects. The test instrumentation showed that the side force in the cockpit was about one "g". No wonder Mike's hand was thrown from the throttle!

On looking back, perhaps we should have foreseen the result. The aileron input needed for level flight provided an abnormal amount of aileron input available for the roll into the heavy wing. In contrast, if the roll had been performed in the opposite direction, it should have proven rather dull.

A major point I took away from this test was to be extremely critical of last minute changes to planned tests which have been developed after much planning and reviewing.

EARLY SR-71 TESTING
by Bob Hoey

In late 1965, I was brought into the highly classified Lockheed SR-71 program, I believe because of my X-15 experience. The airplanes had not yet arrived at Edwards and Maj. Jim Scheuer had been assigned to head up an Air Force flight test evaluation team. AFFTC initially assigned Maj. Charlie Bock as the test pilot and myself as the engineer. Maj. Scheuer had only two or three people working for him at the time and I was asked to help him lay out a test plan that would give the AF a safe but quick look at this new weapon system. After seeing the scope of the testing and the hostile environment of the airplane, I recommended that he try to get a couple more FTE's cleared into the program.

Lockheed's Kelly Johnson ran a tight ship and his method for maintaining tight security was to limit the number of people who had access to information. We had great difficulty learning even the most basic things about the airplane. I suggested to Maj. Scheuer that we try to get a copy of the

Lockheed SR-71 "Blackbird."

Basic Aerodynamic Data Book and a copy of the flight control diagrams. I felt that we could mechanize an engineering simulator and learn an awful lot about the airplane without bothering the Lockheed folks. It was a struggle, but we did gain access to those documents. Capt. Austin Lyons, the chief of the Simulator Branch, was cleared into the program and the two of us immediately went to work to bring an SR-71 engineering simulator on line at Edwards. Security measures forced us to work between 4:30 and midnight, and we had to carefully lock up all data and computer tapes after every evening's work. By the time the aircraft arrived at Edwards Dick Abrams had been assigned as the Performance Engineer and Bob Sudderth had been assigned as the Stability and Control Engineer to work full time on the program. Austin and I continued to support the program with simulator activities.

A review of the SR-71 Aerodynamic Data Book showed that the structure was quite limber. This resulted in significant structural deformation under load that affected the aerodynamics and destabilized the airplane in pitch. These predicted effects were included in our simulation from the outset.

As we were checking out the simulated flight control system we ran into a rather violent control-system-induced vibration at light weight and high airspeed. Although I had a flight control block diagram, I had not been given the location of the gyros and accelerometers in the airplane, but had

191

assumed that they were near the cg. It turned out that the lateral accelerometer was in the nose gear well, about 15 feet forward of the cg. With that correction applied, the simulated control system settled down nicely.

Lockheed had learned from their early flight test work that the cruise drag was considerably higher than predicted. The culprit was apparently a misprediction of the zero lift pitching moment, C_{mo}, which resulted in larger trim drag at cruise speed. Lockheed had devised a modification which raised the flat nose of the airplane about 2 degrees. This would bring the elevons back into trail and regain the lost range. While this modification was being engineered and manufactured, Lockheed wanted to verify their range predictions with the elevons in their correct position. The only way they could bring the elevons into trail BEFORE the new nose was available, was to fly with the cg 2% aft of the published aft limit on the airplane. Their analysis apparently showed that this could be accomplished safely. They flew the flight and lost an airplane at cruise Mach number. When we heard about the accident and identified the flight conditions, we immediately went to our simulator and tried to duplicate the maneuver. Sure enough, we could easily duplicate the loss of control and pitchup that had occurred. The Lockheed test pilot (Bill Weaver, who had survived) and several of their engineers visited our facility one night to confirm our findings. They left soberly nodding their heads.

Shortly after this visit I was invited to accompany the Lockheed stability expert (McMasters) to visit Beale AFB where the first operational SR-71 training simulator was undergoing acceptance. We found several distressing things about their simulator. Many of the important derivatives (such as aileron effectiveness) had been arbitrarily altered to satisfy qualitative comments made by the pilots. Most distressing, however, was the fact that the entire simulation was based solely on the RIGID aerodynamics. At this point in history, training simulators were considered mostly procedural devices. Accuracy in simulating handling qualities was not adequately stressed by the procuring agencies.

Unlike the X-15 simulator, the Edwards SR-71 simulator turned out to be of very little use in planning test missions. Mission duration for the X-15 was about 10 minutes, but for the SR-71 it was several hours - far too long for real-time simulator planning exercises to be profitable. The simulation was of very real value, however, in assessing handling quality trends near the flight boundaries. It was used very effectively to map the single-engine minimum control speed. Throttle chops were accomplished at a safe altitude in the airplane. The dynamics of these maneuvers, including the engine spool-down dynamics, were matched on the simulator, then the maneuver was extrapolated on the simulator to sea level conditions, (higher thrust and yawing moment) thus avoiding the exposure of the airplane to an unnecessary low altitude hazard.

The simulator was also used by Bob Sudderth to perfect a stick-pusher system which I believe was later incorporated in the operational airplane.

§

In 1966 NASA pilot Milt Thompson performed the first successful glide flight of the strange-looking, wingless M2-F2 Lifting Body (a heavy weight version of the earlier M2-F1).

One XB-70A was lost when an F-104 chase airplane contacted one of the drooped wing tips of the giant bomber, and was then swept across the top of the fuselage destroying both vertical fins. Chase pilot Joe Walker and B-70 pilot Carl Cross were killed in the accident.

THE XC-142A'S WINGS POINT UP AND IT FLIES BACKWARDS
by Rob Ransone. Copyright (c) 1995 Ransone Associates, Inc.
Used by permission

The XC-142A looked like a railroad boxcar with short, stubby wings. Its mission requirements to carry an Army truck, but fit on a Navy carrier's elevator, dictated its shape. Built by Ling-Temco-Vought (LTV), it was powered by four GE T64-GE-1 free turbine turboprop engines, swinging large, four-bladed propellers. The requirement to have the entire wing covered by the prop wash, to prevent wing stalls during conversion and STOL operations, resulted in the wings not extending past the outboard propellers. To preclude loss of airflow over the wing during STOL, or loss of thrust from a propeller during VTOL and hover, in the event of an engine failure, a cross-shaft was provided between all four propellers. This meant that all four propellers began turning when the first engine was started. For longitudinal control in VTOL and hover, a small propeller was installed in a horizontal plane just behind the empennage, driven by a shaft through the fuselage, connected to the main propeller cross-shaft at the wing root. During VTOL and hover, the wing was tilted vertically, and lift-off was made by raising a helicopter-type collective lever on the left side of each pilot. Longitudinal control was commanded to the tail prop by moving the control stick fore and aft. Roll control was commanded to right and left engine thrust differentials by lateral stick movements, and yaw control was commanded to aileron deflections by the rudder pedals. When your aircraft had a wing that can point straight up and can fly backwards, you have to expect weird things in its flight control system. After liftoff, a conversion to conventional flight was made by simply pushing the wing-tilt switch forward on the collective lever. The wing came down and the aircraft converted to a real airplane in about ten seconds, flying at 140 knots. An ingenious, fully mechanical box of cams and levers

Hiller/Vought/Ryan XC-142 vertical takeoff and conversion to conventional flight at Edwards South Base.

in the flight control system sorted everything out during transition, and airplane flight used normal aerodynamic controls.

A lot of data in only ten flight test hours

In 1964, the XC-142A was slowly progressing through its Category I tests at the LTV plant in Dallas, Texas, and I was concerned that it would be many months before we had any Government test data. I was also concerned about its suitability for Category II testing because of the many maintenance problems the aircraft had encountered during Category I. I expressed this concern to Major Lou Setter, Chief of Performance Branch. The Navy participates in contractor Category I tests, during its Navy Preliminary Evaluation. How about an MPE (Military Preliminary Evaluation) at LTV? This sounded good, ASD liked the idea, and I wrote a ten-hour flight test plan to be performed at LTV in Dallas. Our evaluation would also include monitoring the maintenance requirements to indicate what was in store for us at Edwards.

We may have set a record for the amount of data obtained in such a short time. Our recorded takeoff, chased by a T-37 airspeed calibration airplane from Edwards, was followed immediately by a check climb to altitude. At the top of the climb, we stabilized on speed-power points while the chase plane calibrated our airspeed system. At the completion of each speed-power point, we did aileron rolls, pitch pulses, and rudder kicks, then did a check descent to the next test altitude. Finally, the flight was completed with a check descent to the field and a recorded landing. We discovered that the aircraft was basically easy to fly and that hover performance was 12 % less than predicted. We identified three safety of flight discrepancies, 22 deficiencies that would curtail our Category II tests if not corrected, 45 deficiencies that, while not needed to allow Category II flight tests, should be corrected and evaluated before Category II was completed, and 43 deficiencies that should be corrected for an operational aircraft. Our 120-page report documented the status of the aircraft, gave ASD preliminary information on the concept, and identified precisely what had to be done to prepare the aircraft for Category II and III tests at Edwards. Time and money well spent.

Why correct your data, when you can test at sea level standard conditions?

Although we had two XC-142As for our Category II tests, I had them both dual instrumented for both performance and stability and control testing in order to get the most test data from each flight. Before we could begin our Category II performance flights tests at Edwards, however, we had to figure out how to reduce the performance data to standard conditions. Should we use airplane data reduction methods, or helicopter methods? OK, helicopter methods for VTOL and hover, and airplane methods for cruise flight - but what about STOL and transition? Helicopter performance data are obtained using density altitude, rather than pressure altitude like conventional airplanes, and the data are presented in coefficient form of CP vs. CT (power coefficient versus thrust coefficient). One chart is all that's needed for all flight conditions. But would this work for tilt-props, and what about the tail prop? Sometimes the tail prop thrust was up, and sometimes it was down, and it would fluctuate continually with pilot longitudinal control movements.

I know! I'll just ignore the tail prop! This solution wasn't as cavalier as it may sound. What I was really doing was assuming that the CP/CT relationship of the tail prop approximated that of the main props, and that any differences would be negligible because the total thrust of the tail prop was a very small percentage of the total thrust of the main props. I didn't mind interpolating hover performance for conditions we had not tested, but I did not want to extrapolate the data. In other words, we needed to be able to hover at the heaviest weights possible in order to get the most data. If you don't have the power, you can't hover. Everybody knows that.

The GE T64-GE-1 engines were design rated at 2850 SHP each, but every engine was exceeding that power on GE's test stands. Therefore, I requested the power test data for the entire fleet of T64 engines, by serial number, and literally hand-picked the eight engines for our two Category II performance and stability and control aircraft. These engines provided from 3200 to 3400 SHP each. We had a real hotrod! Helicopters and VTOL aircraft have pronounced ground effects that vary with disk loading (pounds of aircraft weight per square foot of total rotor or thrusting device area). For helicopters, this is strongly positive — for jet VTOLs this can be strongly negative. We weren't sure what it would be for the XC-142A. For these hover in-ground-effect tests, the XC-142A pilots needed to know how high the wheels were off the ground.

I designed a "Hover Meter" and had Instrumentation Division build it. It consisted of two twenty-foot poles, one with two round disks located at the top and two feet below the top, the other had two cross bars similarly located. Placed a measured distance in line in front of the XC-142A, the pilot could lift off to various wheel heights (6 inches to about 10 feet) that were indicated to him by aligning combinations of bars and disks. Sounds crude, but it worked fine. For our hover tests, I took the aircraft to NAS Pt. Mugu, California, in May 1966, because at that time of the year runway conditions would be very close to sea level and 59 degrees F in the mornings. I had the aircraft loaded to a weight that was above our maximum hover weight, which required special approval from LTV, we set up our "Hover Meter," and started our tests. The aircraft struggled into the air, attaining a wheel height of only two feet. After burning out some fuel, we got up to 30 feet, which was essentially out of ground effect. All of this at essentially sea level, standard conditions. After STOL takeoff and landing tests, we returned to Edwards to study the data.

Sam Barrett, the Air Force "user" pilot on our Tri-Service Test Force, was most grateful for the hover tests at Pt. Mugu — if he had not been at Pt. Mugu, he would have been on the XC-142A in Dallas that crashed during a maximum rate re-conversion to hover, killing the entire LTV flight test crew.

Inventing data reduction methods as we go

STOL takeoffs took about 3.8 seconds, and could be made with the wing incidence angle anywhere between about 5 degrees (the lowest wing angle where the props wouldn't hit the ground), and about 35 degrees. Between 35 and 60 degrees, ground effect recirculation disturbed the aircraft to the extent that the lateral control system could not control it below 25 feet. With all of the variations of power, aircraft weight, wing and flap angles, and atmospheric conditions, how to define the STOL takeoff performance?

After much manipulation of the data, I finally discovered that a specific energy data reduction, $E/(CP/CT)$ vs. ground distance brought all of our

STOL takeoff data down to a single line. What fun!

CHASE 1, CHASE 2........CHASE 6
by Wen Painter

It was right after the XB-70 accident that the rules were changed as to the number of chase planes that could be in the air at any one time. It was on one of the lifting body flights some weeks after the accident that this event happened. Mr. Paul Bikle, Director of the NASA Flight Research Center, where the lifting bodies were located, was in charge of the flight operations of the lifting bodies. Mr. Bikle had a speaker in his office that monitored the ongoing flights that were in operation at NASA FRC. On this day he was working in his office and listening to the test frequency for the lifting body flight. The first call was from the NASA Chase One aircraft, one of the NASA Research Pilots. Then a few minutes later another call was heard, NASA Chase Two airborne, then NASA Chase Three.... At about NASA Chase Five, Mr. Bikle was out of his office on his way down to the pilot's office and looking out the windows at the flight line where he saw several F-104s setting, then he knew he had been had. There was only one chase aircraft in the air at that time, but the same pilot was making all of the calls. One of the NASA Lifting Body Pilots, was flying chase on this flight.

THE LAUNCH CAMERA SIMULATOR
by Wen Painter

During the first launch of the M2-F2 (Flight No. M-1-8) on July 12, 1966 the small camera installed in the adapter looking down at the top of the M2-F2 was not turned on. This was very important to Berwin Kock and myself as we had done all the launch dynamic studies to determine the M2-F2 clearances with respect to the X-15 pylon. Vic Horton, the NASA Flight Test Engineer and Launch Panel Operator on the B-52, had forgotten to turn on the launch camera at the 10 seconds to launch point. This happened to be about the only function that Vic had to do on this flight.

During the next crew briefing, a few weeks later, Berwin and I had made up a small box with a handle (long pencil) on the front of it. We labeled the box "LAUNCH PANEL SIMULATOR." Above the pencil (handle) was labeled "OFF" and at the bottom labeled "ON." This simulator was presented to Vic at the end of the crew briefing with the appropriate speech and was placed in front of him. Vic was always in on all the jokes on people around the center, but was not one who liked jokes being played on him. Vic sat there looking at the "simulator" as the speech was made, then he reached up and hit the handle (pencil) down to the "ON" position. From the bottom of the box, in which we had cut a little opening, a banana rolled out. The whole room roared with laughter and Vic could only set there and shake his head, then he took the banana and threw it at Berwin and myself. He NEVER forgot to turn on the launch camera switch after that.

§

As part of the Apollo program to land a man on the moon, a giant Saturn V booster was launched from Cape Canaveral for the first time in 1967. The program received a major setback later in the year, however, when 3 astronauts were killed in a fire on the launch pad during a training exercise. Meanwhile out at Edwards, Major "Pete" Knight, flying a modified X-15, reached a new record speed for winged airplanes of 6.7 times the speed of sound.

EXPANDING THE X-15 ENVELOPE TO MACH 6.7
by Johnny Armstrong

On October 3 1967 the X-15A-2 research aircraft achieved a maximum Mach number of 6.72 piloted by Major Pete Knight. The events that led up to the flight really began five years earlier when, on its 31st flight, the number two X-15, S/N 66671, suffered major damage during an emergency landing at Mud Lake, Nevada.

Ten months prior to that emergency landing I had returned to Edwards as a civilian employee for AFFTC. Following my four years at Edwards in flight test engineering wearing the AF blue, I had accepted a job with NASA at Huntsville Alabama during which time I had worked on flight test of the Saturn rocket vehicle. Then near the end of 1961 I was contacted to see if I would be interested in returning to Edwards to work on the X-15. That was an easy yes. I had been missing airplanes so much that I would run out of the house to see the Southern Airways DC-3 fly over. So here I was back at Edwards working as the AFFTC flight planner on one of the most exciting programs of all times.

The ship 2 X-15 had entered the three-ship X-15 program in September 1959. In 1961 it had flown nine flights reaching a maximum Mach number of 6.04 and a max altitude of 217,000 feet.

X-15 crash landing at Mud Lake
NASA pilot Jack McKay had just launched from the B-52 mothership at 45,000 feet, lit the YLR-99 rocket engine and was on his way when Pete Knight, who was the flight communicator in the NASA control room, radioed for him to check his throttle position. Jack verified it was at the full throttle position and Pete advised him that the engine was only putting out 30 percent thrust.

This kind of situation is exactly why all X-15 flights were launched

North American X-15 (ship #2) at Mud Lake after landing accident.

within gliding distance of a suitable dry lakebed. When Pete radioed that it was going to be a Mud Lake landing, Jack began a preplanned series of actions to make an emergency landing. He shutdown the engine and set up the turning pattern to Mud Lake, jettisoning the anhydrous ammonia and liquid oxygen propellants along the way. Due to several of Mr. Murphy's law things adding together, the strut of the left main landing gear failed on touchdown resulting in the aircraft turning sideways and then rolling upside down trapping Jack in his seat with his head next to the lakebed surface. Prior to rolling over Jack had had the forethought to jettison the canopy. The emergency crew that was pre-stationed at the site immediately moved into action. The Air Force helicopter pilot had the good judgment to hover over the X-15 blowing away the pungent fumes of the anhydrous ammonia still venting from the aircraft. The ground crew was able to dig a hole in the lakebed to provide enough clearance to extract Jack from the cockpit and get him on the way for medical attention. Jack would live to fly the X-15 again but he was an inch shorter due to crushed vertebra.

Six months after the Mud Lake landing accident a contract was signed with North American to repair and modify the aircraft to an advanced configuration to accomplish future experiments. The modified aircraft was returned to Edwards in February 1964 and made its first flight in June of that year. The main modification to the aircraft was the addition of two jettisonable external tanks to hold added engine propellant to provide a Mach 8 capability. This additional performance was desired for testing of a hypersonic ram-jet engine then under development by NASA Langley. The airplane had also been lengthened by 29 inches to add room for a tank to provide hydrogen fuel for the ramjet engine. Other modifications included additional hydrogen peroxide tanks for propellant turbopumps for the longer engine burn time of about an additional 60 seconds, an openable hatch behind the cockpit for a star tracker experiment, and a modified canopy windshield. Additionally, an ablative coating was developed to be applied to the aircraft to protect the structure from the higher heating that would be encountered during the higher Mach number flights.

The envelope expansion effort began with Flight 43 when Major Rushworth flew the first flight with external tanks. Consistent with the incremental approach of an envelope expansion program this flight was flown with the external tanks empty. Now there was a new constraint for the X-15 flight. The launch point not only had to be the necessary distance from Edwards depending on the max Mach to be flown, and also within gliding distance of a prepared dry lakebed runway, but also had to have a suitable area for the tanks to impact upon being jettisoned after they were empty. For this flight the X-15 was launched near Cuddeback dry lake about 60 miles North of Edwards on a heading that would result in the external tanks impacting on the Edwards bombing range. The flight was flown at 50 percent thrust to slow the acceleration. The flight went about as planned with the tanks being jettisoned at Mach 2.2 and 70,000 feet. The tanks impacted on the bombing range. The recovery chute system work properly for the ammonia tank and it was recovered in repairable condition. The LOX tank recovery chute did not deploy and the tank was destroyed on impact. With this flight the handling qualities of the X-15 with external tanks were verified to be adequate although somewhat worse than the simulator. It also validated the tank ejection and separation.

We See No Flow
Now we were ready to fly with full external tanks to Mach 6.0. It was to be the 45th flight of ship 2. It was also going to be last flight for Major Rushworth who had received his orders for his next assignment. (Rushworth flew more flights in the X-15 than any other pilot; a total of 34.) In retrospect, with twenty-twenty hindsight, flight 45 was destined for failure. The propellants were pumped to the engine from the internal tanks of the X-15 and the propellants in the external tanks were just pressure transferred into the internal tanks. From simulation studies we knew that the pilot would lose control of the X-15 rather rapidly if one of the tanks failed to transfer propellant. This was simply due to the moment that would be pro-

duced about the roll axis that could not be counteracted by the X-15 roll control that was produced by the differential deflection of the horizontal tails. We developed procedures in the simulator to be followed if one of the tanks failed to feed after launch. It essentially consisted of immediately setting up at conditions of angle of attack and dynamic pressure where tanks separation was predicted to be good. This consisted of first shutting down the engine, maintaining angle of attack to let the dynamic pressure decrease below 400 psf and then pushing over to low angle of attack and jettisoning the tanks. Then a landing would be made at Mud Lake. We practiced this over and over and over again in the simulator with Jack McKay serving as NASA 1, the flight controller. A few seconds after launch we would simulate the failure and Jack would make the canned call "we see no flow" and Rushworth would then initiate his abort actions.

We knew that the instrumentation available to establish that the tanks were feeding was an indirect indication, but it was felt that adequate pre-launch test would validate the instrumentation. This instrumentation was a pressure transducer across an orifice in the helium lines that pressurized each of the external tanks. (We had better instrumentation under development but it was not available for this flight.) We had verified the pressure transducer operation during a planned captive flight with propellants in the external tanks. At the four-minute-to-launch point on flight 45 we verified that the pressure sensors were working satisfactorily by jettisoning a small amount of propellant. After launch on flight 45 the ammonia-helium pressure did not respond. As a result, 18 seconds after launch Jack announced over the radio the dreaded call, "We see no flow on Ammonia Bob." Bob immediately began setting up to jettison the tanks. He reduced the throttle to minimum thrust and pushed over to the desired 6 degrees angle of attack then hit the tank jettison switch. He forgot that he had not shut down the engine and proceeded to do so. The tanks separated cleanly although at much higher dynamic pressure than desired. The emergency landing at Mud lake was as routine as an emergency landing in an X-15 could be. Post flight analysis led to the conclusion that the fuel was, in fact, feeding from the ammonia tank properly. I carried the lesson learned from this flight with me for the rest of my active flight test career. Do not make critical flight decisions on inadequate/marginal instrumentation!

The next flight (49) was flown with the ventral fin on to Mach 5.2. It was primarily to familiarize Pete Knight with the handling qualities in this configuration that would be flown on the following flight with external tanks. Flight 50 was the first successful flight with propellant in the external tanks. Improved propellant transfer sensors (paddle switches) were installed for this flight. The flight was flown as planned and reached a max Mach of 6.3.

Flight 51 was flown to evaluate the aircraft's handling qualities with a dummy ramjet installed on the fixed portion of the lower ventral fin. The dummy ramjet was jettisoned during final approach as was normal for the movable lower rudder due to lack of adequate ground clearance for landing. The flight was flown without external tanks and reached a Mach number of 4.8. Next was a flight with the ablative coating and dummy ramjet installed but without external tanks. The flight was flown to Mach 5 and the ablative generally performed as expected although there were indications of high heating in the lower ventral fin adjacent to the ramjet that we did not fully appreciate until the next flight. The ablative coating was refurbished and the aircraft prepared for its "all up" flight with external tanks, ablative coating, and dummy ramjet.

Fastest airplane flight of the Century

All was ready on the morning of 3 October 1967 as Col Joe Cotton started each of the eight engines on the NB-52B mothership affectionately named "Balls Eight" from its S/N 008. Pete had already been in the small cockpit of the X-15 for over an hour performing the pre-flight checks with the ground crew led by Charlie Baker and Larry Barnett and a host of test support personnel in the NASA control room. After takeoff of the B-52/X-15 with Maj Cuthill following in an F-104 as chase 1, it took about 50 minutes to reach the launch point abeam Mud Lake approximately 170 nautical miles north of Edwards.

"I reached up and hit the launch switch and immediately took my hand off to go back to the throttle and found I had not gone anywhere. It did not launch. So I probably just got my hand off of it, because I reached up and hit it again and it launched the second time. Launch was very smooth this time."

As the X-15 was falling from the B-52 he lit the engine and locked on to 12 degrees angle of attack. He was pushed back into his seat with 1.5 g's longitudinal acceleration. The X-15 rounded the corner and started its climb. During the rotation as normal acceleration built up to 2 g's Pete had to hold in considerable right deflection of the side arm controller to keep the X-15 from rolling to the left due to the heavier LOX in the left external tank. When the aircraft reached the planned pitch angle of 35 degrees his scan pattern switched from the angle of attack gage to the attitude direction indicator and a vernier index that was set to the precise climb angle. The climb continued as the fuel was consumed from the external tanks, then at about 60 seconds he reached the tank jettison conditions of about Mach 2 and 70,000 feet. He pushed over to low angle of attack and ejected the tanks. He was now on his way and would not be making an emergency landing at Mud

North American X-15A-2 with ablative coating, external tanks, and dummy ramjet.

Lake. "We shut down at 6500 (fps), and I took careful note to see what the final got to. It went to 6600 maximum on the indicator. As I told Johnny before, the longest time period is going to be from zero h dot getting down to 100 to 200 feet per second starting down hill after shutdown." Final post flight data recorded an official max Mach number of 6.72 equivalent to a speed of 4534 miles per hour. From there down Pete was very busy with the planned data maneuvers and managing the energy of the gliding X-15. He approached Edwards higher on energy than planned and had to keep the speed brakes out to decelerate. On final approach he pushed the dummy ramjet eject button and landed on Rogers lakebed runway 18. He indicated he did not feel anything when he activated the ramjet eject and the ground crew reported they did not see it. Pete said that he knew something was not right when the recovery crew did not come to the cockpit area to help him out of the cockpit, but went directly to the back of the airplane. Finally when he did get out and saw the damage to the tail of the X-15 he understood. There were large holes in the skin of the sides of the fin with evidence of melting and skin rollback. Now we are talking Inconel-X steel that melts at 2200 degrees F. Later analysis would show that the shock wave from the leading edge of the ramjet's spike nose had intersected the fin and caused the aerodynamic heating to increase seven times higher than normal. So now maybe we knew why the ramjet was not there.

X-15 dummy ramjet search

"I did not feel anything when I pushed the button for the ramjet. I understand that there were people saw that it did come off and others say that they never saw it, so I don't know where it is." So said Major Pete Knight during the postflight debriefing.

The flight records indicated that the ramjet instrumentation ceased functioning 25 seconds after the engine was shutdown and the airplane reached Mach 6.72. So at about Mach 6 during the deceleration/glide the burn through had taken place. The obvious conclusion then was that the ramjet departed at that time and had gone it's merry way from over 90,000 feet to the desert floor below; over 100 miles from Edwards.

Later that afternoon as several of us were reviewing the data records we noted an abnormal decrease in the sensitive longitudinal acceleration trace (indicating a sudden decrease in drag). Although it was a small change, it was instantaneous. We decided to go on the assumption that this could be where the ramjet departed the airplane. Correlating the time of day with the flight parameters we found that it was at about the 180 degree point during the turn over the south area of Rogers Lake bed at about Mach 1.0 and 32,000 feet. The airplane was in a 57 degree left bank and, more importantly, pulling 1.6 g. Now I was confident that this could have been the time that the dummy ramjet began it's independent trajectory. So next, I time-correlated the radar data and found the spot where this event occurred and the heading of the aircraft at the time. This then was the Initial Conditions of the ramjet flight. Next, I drew a line on a map along the heading at the time I suspected it separated from the X-15. I could say that I did a detailed calculation of the drag coefficient for a tumbling ramjet, then a 5th order curve fit of the potential trajectory, corrected for winds; — but actually, I just made an engineering estimate (guess) at a downrange distance. It turned out that the estimated resting place was right on the Edwards AFB bombing range. Placing a mark on the map at my selected impact point, I then drew a line perpendicular to the estimated track. Next I picked out some recognizable ground reference points on the map. As it turned out I selected the Rocket Base on Luehman Ridge east of Rogers Dry Lakebed and a mountain peak in the San Bernardino mountains.

Now it was time to present my theory to the team. There were many disbeliever's of the theory who felt the dummy ramjet was way up north of Edwards. However, Bill Albrecht, the NASA Operations Engineer in charge of X-15A-2, was willing to humor and trust me. We contacted Joe Rief, the AFFTC airfield manager, and got permission to go wandering out on the bombing range. Bill and I got in a NASA radio equipped carryall van, radioed Eddie Tower, and headed out on the range. We drove east on the road on

Dummy ramjet installed on X-15A-2 prior to record-setting flight.

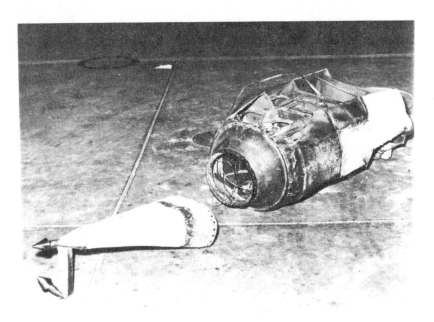

Dummy ramjet found on Edwards bombing range following record-break-ing flight.

the bombing range with me looking for that general area where I had drawn the line on the map. We finally stopped the van and we walked down the road until I could hold my arms out and line up the Rocket Base and the mountain peak. At that point, I had Bill head North-East along my magic line and I headed South-West.

Shock! Disbelief! Glee! Cold chills up my spine! After walking only about 200 yards, I saw the ramjet lying on the sand in between the tumble weed bushes in two major pieces. I hollered with excitement to Bill but he was out of hearing range. So I ran back to the road and got his attention and we managed to back track to where I had seen it. There was a depression in the sand back up the track where it made first contact before coming to rest. We gathered up the nose cone and the machined conical steel pressure probes that were the very leading edge of the ramjet and headed back to the van. The main body of the dummy ramjet was too large and heavy for us to return. It was almost quitting time at NASA when we carried our trophy up to the pilot's office. I strutted around like the hen that laid the golden egg. Fitz Fulton, I recall was favorably impressed. The next day Albrecht and I went back out to the site to direct a Huey helicopter to the location. A cable was attached to the main part of the ramjet and it was flown back to NASA.

Inspection of the ramjet revealed that it also had major melting and damage due to the high aerodynamic heating in the area where it attached to the ventral fin. In addition, 3 of the 4 explosive bolts that held the ramjet on had been fired, undoubtedly due to the high temperature. The fourth bolt had structurally failed; which was apparently all that was securing the ramjet on the X-15 from about Mach 6 down to Mach 1.

The X-15 program winds down

There was major damage to the structure of the fixed lower ventral fin from excessive aerodynamic heating due to shock wave impingement from the nose of the dummy ramjet. The aircraft was trucked to North American Aviation at LAX to be repaired, however it was to never fly again. Six months after the Mach 6.72 flight of ship 2 the Number 3 X-15 crashed near Randsburg, California killing Major Mike Adams. Over the next year the number 1 X-15 flew eight more flights with the last flight occurring on 24 October 1968, the 199th flight of the X-15 program. Several attempts were made to fly the 200th flight but to no avail. On 20 December Pete Knight was in the cockpit of the X-15 under the wing of Balls Eight ready to taxi to the runway when a freak snow storm moved over Edwards and the flight was cancelled. Thus ended the flying portion of the most successful X-plane program in history, however the analysis of the research data from the program continued for many years afterward.

How did I get involved in all this?· RPRT. I was fortunate to be the Air Force flight planner during this time period on the X-15 program. I got to develop the flight plan using the X-15 man-in-the-loop simulator, train the pilots and then participate in the control room during the flight. Throughout my flight test career RPRT was good to me and allowed me to participate in some major flight test events and programs. It also presented me with the opportunity to work with some of the top people in the flight test community and this thing we called the test team. The AFFTC/NASA FRC X-15 team was one of the best.

RPRT? - RIGHT PLACE RIGHT TIME.

A MOST DIFFICULT AIRCRAFT TO MAINTAIN
by Rob Ransone. Copyright (c) 1995 Ransone Associates, Inc.
Used by permission

An advantage of the XC-142A designation, over the X- designation that it should have had, was that it gave the illusion of being about ready for production. A big disadvantage of the designation was that people expected it to be about ready for production. In fact, maintainability and reliability were specifically not included in the design requirements in order to reduce its cost. Big mistake. As a result, the mean time before failure was only about ten minutes. Vibration was the major culprit that broke fuel lines, wires and brackets, and cracked structure. LTV set up a special vibration test rig, using aircraft # 5, in which they shook the aircraft at all of the forcing frequencies. With four four-bladed props operating at two different RPM, and a three-bladed prop at the tail operating at another RPM — there was a forcing natural frequency for virtually everything in the aircraft!

LTV set up lagged-synched strobe lights with which they could walk around the aircraft cargo compartment and watch the cables and components writhing in slow motion. They would then tag the component with its natural frequency. It was like walking through snakes — quite a sight! In the meantime, at Edwards, I was cataloging all of the failures logged by maintenance for our entire Category II and III flight tests. This was before handy little computers, so I had to do it by hand. I made up a box of 3x5 index cards on which I had noted the failures according to system (hydraulic, electrical, flight control, etc.), location (wing, nacelle, tail, center fuselage, etc.), and component (bracket, hydraulic line, wire, structure, etc.). Gay Jones, the project pilot, and I then went to LTV to discuss what should be done to the remaining aircraft to enable them to safely complete the remaining flight tests.

With the results of LTV's vibration tests, and my box of index cards, we sat down with Gale Swan, LTV's Chief Engineer, and went through XC-142A systems item by item. At issue was which components to "zero-time" and which to just continue to monitor. Zero-timing everything would cost too much money and time. For example, we considered a wiring harness in the nacelle. The vibration tests showed that it was in resonance with the four per rev forcing frequency from the prop, my index cards showed a high failure rate for wires in the nacelle next to the props — put in a new one! How about a control cable in the aft fuselage? It was vibrating considerably, but we had no record of cable failures and the aft fuselage was relatively benign — leave it alone! The result of this analysis allowed the # 5 airplane, when it went to NASA Langley, to fly fifteen hours before its first hydraulic leak. An incredible improvement.

§

After 199 flights spanning 9 years, the X-15 research program was brought to a conclusion in late 1968.

MY F-104 FLIGHT
by Bob Hoey

I was the AFFTC Project Engineer for the X-15 during the first two years of the 9-year flight test program. I continued to stay close to the program even while I moved into the supervisory chain at the AFFTC. In the spring of 1968 we received short notice of a high level meeting that was to take place at NASA Ames (Moffett Field), Cal. Major Pete Knight, the AFFTC Project Pilot at the time, suggested that he and I schedule a two-seater F-104 and make a quick trip up and back to attend the meeting. (I was the stability and control project engineer for the AF tests of the F-104A in 1957, but it was a

F-104 takeoff with landing gear retracting.

single seater so I had never had a ride in an F-104.)

While taxiing out we discovered that the mike in my headset was intermittent. I could hear Pete, but he couldn't always hear me. Just after liftoff I heard an expletive from the front seat. I glanced around the cockpit and saw two barber poles on the main gear. Pete explained that the ground crew had been having difficulty adjusting the microswitches on the main gear doors on this particular airplane. He figured that the wheels were up but that the doors were still hanging open. No big problem except we would have to stay below the 296 knot gear-down speed all the way to Moffett rather than the supersonic dash I was hoping for.

The weather forecast for Moffett was about 1500 ft. overcast for our arrival. When we reached our letdown point Pete called in to the enroute traffic controllers to give them our position. While he was talking the radio gradually faded out and quit. The standard procedure for a radio failure is to proceed according to your planned IFR flight plan. Luckily the navigation radio was still working so Pete made a VOR penetration through the clouds and we broke out about 1500 feet above the ground still about 15 miles from Moffett. Pete advised me that if the engine coughed, I should eject immediately since he wasn't going to wait for me. We bored along under the overcast with our gear doors hanging until we spotted the airport. He made a pass down the runway waggling the wings (a standard signal to the tower that we were without a radio), circled and landed. We taxied in with the usual "emergency" array of fire trucks, ambulances, etc., in trail, then rushed off to our meeting.

Since Moffett was a Navy base they didn't have any capability to fix either gear doors or radios on an Air Force F-104. When the meeting finished we were both in a sour mood since the NASA management had just decided to forego the Langley ramjet flight demonstration and, as a result, to close down the X-15 flight test program. Pete solved the transportation-home problem by calling Test Operations at Edwards and requesting one of the other pilots to fly another F-104 to Moffett. We were then able to file a return formation flight as a "flight of 2," relying on the radio in the other F-104. Pete and I boarded the 2-seater 104 and took off with no radio and with the gear doors still hanging open. We flew formation with the other F-104 all the way back to Edwards at 296 knots. The weather had cleared so it actually was a fairly pleasant flight. I got a chance to do a little formation flying and Pete demonstrated an X-15 low L/D landing approach to the lakebed when we got home.

HL-10 WITH USAF DECALS
by Wen Painter

(Editors note: Flight testing of the three Lifting Bodies was performed by a joint Air Force/NASA test team even though the HL-10 and M2-F2 were purchased solely with NASA money, while the X-24A was purchased solely with Air Force money.)

This is a story about the time large USAF decals appeared on each side of the HL-10 Lifting Body. One Monday morning when the HL-10 ground crew arrived at the NASA Flight Research Center hanger about 7:30 A.M. they found the large USAF decals placed on each side of the vehicle. The top management was notified by the crew chief, Charlie Russell, and by 7:35 A.M. the decals were removed.

There had been a lot of discussion by the Air Force Lifting Body pilot as to why the X-24A had USAF on each side of the vehicle and NASA painted on top of each vertical fin, which was standard on almost all of the NASA aircraft. An "Official Retouched Photo" was released later with two Air Force Officers in the photo of the HL-10 with USAF painted on the side of the vehicle. The title on the photo was "The Midnight Skulker Strikes Again."

The Air Force Lifting Body Pilot Jerauld R. Gentry was always suspect as the person who placed the decals on the HL-10 Lifting Body.

HL-10 Lifting Body and the "Midnight Skulkers" (Capt. Charles Archie and Capt. "Jerry" Gentry).

THE GREEN ZINC CHROMATE CAR
by Wen Painter

The story starts when USAF Lifting Body Pilot Jerauld "Jerry" Gentry was looking at the inside of the M2-F2 Lifting Body one day out in the NASA hanger. The inside of the lifting body was painted with a green zinc chromate paint to protect it from corrosion, which is standard for most aircraft. Jerry commented that he hated that color, because he had a pair of pants that color when he was younger. On one of Jerry's lifting body flights a few weeks later, after the B-52 had taxied out for take off, the M2-F2 mechanics and other members of the crew took his 1954 Ford and pushed it out to the NASA paint shop. The car was promptly painted green zinc chromate and was returned back to the parking spot next to the NASA hanger. When the debriefing was over and Jerry came down to get his car and return back to his Air Force office, he found his car painted in his most hated color. Jerry couldn't believe that it was completed within less than two hours. On his next flight the same car was covered with "hippy" flower decals, which were quite popular in that time period. The car was a real standout around Edwards AFB during the next couple of years, before he was reassigned to Vietnam.

TWO LIFTING BODY FLIGHTS ON THE SAME B-52
ON THE SAME DAY
by Wen Painter

On April 17, 1969 two lifting bodies were flown on the same day using the same B-52 carrier aircraft.

The first flight (very early in the morning) was the first launch flight (Flight No. X-1-2) of the X-24A with USAF Pilot Captain Jerauld "Jerry" Gentry. The second flight later in the afternoon was the HL-10 (Flight No. H-15-27) with John Manke, NASA Pilot at the controls. The B-52 Pilot on both flights was USAF Col. Emil "Ted" Sturmthal. The controller for both of these flights was NASA Pilot Bill Dana.

By the time the debriefings were over, it was time to head for the Edwards AFB Officer's Club and start celebrating the event. Martin Marietta Corp., the builder of the X-24A Lifting Body, furnished the refreshments for the evening. As time and partying went on the crowd grew larger, then came the tradition of throwing the pilots in the pool. The first to go was USAF Pilot Jerry Gentry, the X-24A pilot, then NASA Pilot John Manke. The next was NASA Pilot Bill Dana, the controller for both flights that day, and then

Lifting Body test pilots and HL-10. L to r: Capt. "Jerry" Gentry, Capt. "Pete" Hoag, John Manke, Bill Dana.

the USAF B-52 Pilot Col. Ted Sturmthal. It took about 10 men (most were fighter pilots) to get Ted into the pool, Ted was about 6 foot 4 inches and about 220 pounds. When Ted crawled out of the pool and came back into the lounge the General was standing there and said, "Ted, I thought that you bombers pilots were smarter than fighter pilots." Ted stood there dripping wet and said, "This is what a few free drinks will get you." Up to this point all the pilots were still in their flight suits, and their billfolds were removed before they were tossed into the pool.

The party was now getting into high gear, the next person to go into the pool was John McTigue, the NASA Lifting Body Project Manager. He had just bought a very expensive suit and it was the first time he had worn it, but didn't matter; he went in the pool any way. The next person to go into the pool was the NASA Operations Engineer Norman DeMar, and then the NASA Chief of Aircraft Operations Stanley Butchart, who fought very hard but went into the pool anyway. The person leading the way, selecting the people to throw into the pool, was one of the USAF Lifting Body Pilots by the name of Capt. Peter "Pete" Hoag. After Stan Butchart pulled himself out of the pool, Pete was calling for throwing the General into the pool. The General stepped up and said, "Boys, the party is over!" That is when most of us went home. It was getting late anyway, since most of us had come to work about 03:00 A.M. that morning.

US/FEDERAL REPUBLIC OF GERMANY (FRG)
JOINT FLIGHT TEST GROUP
by Carl D. Simmons

I was assigned to the US/FRG Flight Test Group in Manching, W. Germany in the latter part of the 1960s. Our assignment was to evaluate the VTOL aircraft that were being developed by the W. Germans. There was another group in the US evaluating the VTOL aircraft being developed in the US. The aircraft we were concerned with were the VJ-101, the Do-31, the VAK191, and the US/FRG fighter. The company test pilots for the VJ-101 and the Do-31 were both American whereas a W. German was the company test pilot for the VAK-191. Language was not a particular problem. Most of the Germans were proficient in English; however, in preparation for this assignment, I had attended a total immersion language course. Initially a technical translator was assigned to me for the more difficult meetings. It was sometimes difficult to stay focused when the translator was simultaneously translating the speaker's words during the meetings. The US/FRG Fighter was in early development whereas there was hardware for the other three. In each of the hardware programs a "bedstead" was developed to flight test the control system. Each program used an attitude control system rather than the rate control system used by such aircraft as the British-made Harrier and the US-made XC-142. The aircraft attitude varied with the stick or control column position. Additionally, there was a rapid site development program on-going with a US contractor at the site.

During the evaluation of one flying bedstead, a US pilot almost lost it, getting into a "JC" maneuver. This was, of course, reported. When the problem had been resolved to the contractor's satisfaction, they offered the vehicle for retest but only by the pilot who had initially reported the problem. Test Ops at Edwards didn't like anyone telling them who was going to be assigned to a project. They almost created an international incident by insisting that a different pilot would be assigned. We finally prevailed and Major Tom Smith came back to find that the problem had been resolved.

Pipes were joined together to form various portions of the flying bedsteads. The engine arrangements of the bedsteads represented those of the developed vehicles. The engines were vertically mounted in a fixed position. On the real aircraft, some of the engines would swivel or rotate to achieve conventional flight after a vertical takeoff. For safety, the bedsteads were initially tested on a device called a telescope and again after significant control system changes. The telescope was a gimballed arrangement that allowed attitude changes while the bedstead was safely anchored. One find ing from the bedstead tests was that pilot evaluations were significantly affected by their perception of the cockpit. For example, pilot ratings increased when the lower part of the cockpit was enclosed so that the pilot had the effect of a canopy rail.

The Do-31 was a cargo-type VTOL aircraft developed by Dornier Aircraft Corporation. It had four vertically mounted jet engines in a pod at each wing tip. Additionally, the main engines were equipped with swiveling thrust nozzles so that the thrust could be rotated from full aft to 30 degrees forward of vertical. This aircraft had a conventional as well as a VTOL capability. During testing for the conventional takeoff, the nosewheel shimmy potential was evaluated. The requirement was for a specific ground speed. Therefore we decided to try a pace car. I owned a Chrysler equipped with a cruise control that could be preset for a desired speed and then engaged at any speed for acceleration to the preset speed. The Chrysler accelerated ahead of the aircraft and at the preset speed, the turn signal was activated to signal the pilot. The pilot then activated the charges on the nosegear to stimulate any shimmy response.

There was a lot of excitement during the nosewheel shimmy tests. On one occasion I thought the airspeed boom was going to shake off the airplane. During that test the cameras showed clearly that the fuselage was being deformed by the magnitude of the forces from the nosewheel system — the skin actually looked wrinkled in the movies. There was no permanent damage to the airplane during these tests even though there was a lot of shaking going on. We repeated the tests after changes were made in the nose gear structure and castor/camber. There were no further problems.

A Rapid Site Development Program, with a US contractor, was to provide a capability to operate these VTOL aircraft in remote areas. Without some form of site hardening, the vertically mounted engines would have rapidly eroded any unprepared surface. The VJ-101 had two afterburning jet engines in each wingtip pod and therefore, posed the most severe requirement in terms of velocity. On one occasion, the aircraft took off from the Rapid Site pad and hovered over it. When the aircraft moved slightly off the center of the pad, the roughly 20,000-pound pad started shaking like you would shake a blanket. The pad was subsequently anchored all around and used quite successfully in the Do-31 program.

The programs were conducted at three different locations; therefore, we moved around the countryside quite a bit. Sometimes we encountered situations outside the norm. On one occasion, I was driving an official US vehicle near the W. German Flight Test Center at Manching. There was a lot of fog. I had cautiously passed this moped-type vehicle just before I came to a railroad crossing with the gate down. While sitting there waiting for the train there was a knock on the driver's side window and I rolled it down to see a farmer on the moped. After a few introductory words, the man informed me that he disagreed with President Johnson's policies in Vietnam. All I could say was "thank you very much." I did relay this message to our contact at the Embassy. On another occasion, I encountered a stranded motorist on the autobahn when it was very cold. After assuring the passengers were in a warm place, I assisted the driver in obtaining mechanical assistance for the vehicle. For this, I subsequently received a gift labeling me a "Cavalier of the Strasse." Oh well, it was all contained in that famous part of our Job Description entitled "Other duties as required."

In 1969 the remaining XB-70A was flown to Wright Patterson Air Force Base by "Fitz" Fulton and Col. Ted Sturmthal to take its place in the Air Force Museum. One of the X-15's, its mission also completed, arrived at the Smithsonian's National Air and Space Museum.

President Kennedy's ambitious technology challenge was successfully accomplished as Neil Armstrong and "Buzz" Aldrin landed on the moon, then returned to earth during the Apollo 11 mission.

FIRST SUPERSONIC LIFTING BODY FLIGHT
by Robert W. Kempel

I was assigned as the lead stability, control, and handling qualities engineer on the joint NASA/USAF HL-10 rocket powered lifting body program. NASA's John Manke was one of the participating program pilots and was scheduled to make the first supersonic lifting body flight. The flight was scheduled for early May 1969.

The flight plan called for a launch approximately 30 miles northeast of Edwards, the ignition of three of the four rocket chambers, rotation to an angle of attack (AOA) of 20 deg., maintain 20 deg. AOA until pitch attitude was 40 deg., maintain 40 deg. pitch attitude until an altitude of 50,000 feet was reached. At 50,000 feet, pushover to 6 deg. AOA and accelerate to a Mach number of 1.08. This was to be followed by altering AOA and turning off another rocket chamber and maintaining constant Mach number while gathering data. Maximum Mach number was to be 1.08. Landing was to be a typical lifting body 360 deg. overhead approach with a landing on Rogers lake bed runway 18.

The actual flight went almost according to plan. John later reported that during the flight there were no significant problems and that "everything went real well." There were the usual comments concerning the pre-flight checks, the flight and comparisons with the simulator and the landing approach. In general everything went totally according to plan. This was significantly different than the ground simulation preparations for this flight.

Some very interesting events occurred leading up to this first lifting body supersonic flight. Engineering preparations leading up to the first lifting body supersonic flight included the following events. In preparation for the flight a complete review of the wind tunnel aerodynamic data was accomplished. In addition, a reassessment of the predicted vehicle stability and controllability characteristics in the transonic and low supersonic flight regimes was completed. Between the Mach numbers of 0.9 and 1.0 the aerodynamic data indicated an area of low to slightly negative directional stability at angles of attack of 25.5 deg. and above. Predictions and the simulator results indicated acceptable levels of longitudinal and lateral-directional dynamic stability at all angles of attack and Mach numbers. A detailed Technical Briefing was planned and presented to NASA and Air Force management teams. The HL-10, and lifting bodies in general, had very high levels of effective dihedral and this, in combination with positive angles of attack and acceptable levels of directional stability, insured lateral-directional Dutch roll dynamic stability everywhere in the flight envelope. It was demonstrated that the HL-10 would exhibit Dutch roll stability even if the directional stability was zero or even slightly negative provided the angle of attack didn't approach zero. this was due in part to the high level of effective dihedral that

Northrop HL-10 in powered flight.

existed. To demonstrate this to our project pilot we set the directional stability to zero (a gross modification) at all Mach numbers and AOA in a special simulation aerodynamic data set. To prove our point we then allowed the pilot to "fly" this simulated HL-10 around the flight envelope. What we failed to tell John was that the vehicle would remain stable if the AOA remained at some positive value and not allowed to approach zero. We successfully demonstrated to John that even with this, purely fictitious, gross adjustment to the data set, the HL-10 would remain dynamically stable.

John, being the diligent test pilot he was, and as fate would have it, was in the simulator during his lunch hour (brown bag beside him) practicing for the first supersonic flight. At this particular simulation session, no program engineers were in attendance and substitute simulation engineer inadvertently loaded the wrong aerodynamic data set into the computer; the data set with the directional stability set to zero. This was the demonstration data set and should not have been used for flight planning. John didn't realize that the wrong data set was in the simulator. With his task complete the simulation engineer departed for lunch. He left John on his own, thinking "what could possibly go wrong, all John had to do was hit the operate and reset switches."

As the simulator run progressed and John achieved the planned altitude for the acceleration to supersonic speed, he pushed the nose over (toward zero AOA) and lo-and-behold the vehicle became violently unstable lateral-directionally. The flight plan called for John to pushover to only 6 deg. AOA, but he must have inadvertently approached AOA near 0 deg. John "crashed" in the simulator. Needless to say this got John's immediate attention! Not knowing exactly what to do John expressed his intense concerns to NASA management before reporting the problem to the program engineers, who were off having lunch some place.

Before the program engineers knew what was happening, we were all summoned, somewhat bewildered, to one of the wood-paneled executive offices (The "Bikle barrel" as we called it in honor of our Director Mr. Paul Bikle). So there we were standing in the boss's office, in a corner, trying to explain why we were trying to kill a perfectly good research pilot, a guy we all kinda liked even if he was from South Dakota. The scene was turning ugly! We can remember that the door seemed like such a long distance from where we were and a formidable barrier of high level managers stood between us and it. We were obviously judged guilty and all that remained was for the sentence to be passed! Those in attendance from the project were Garry Layton, Wen Painter, Berwin Kock, and Bob Kempel. From the management side there were Paul Bikle, Joe Weil, Jack Fischel, et al. John, the project pilot, was not among the crowd. After the feeding frenzy abated, we were given our "day in court." It dawned on us what had happened! It was all a mistake!! We explained the problem and followed this up with a demonstration in the simulation lab. Needless to say, once that the correct aero data set was loaded into the simulator the situation was much improved and NO dynamic instability was encountered (as predicted) either in the simulation or in flight! We were exonerated! We again (remembering the words of Dr. Hugh L. Dryden) separated the real from the imagined and made known the overlooked!! In this situation we project engineers were the victims of

221

the unexpected!

This story is indicative of how at least one of the pilots viewed the simulation once credibility was established; he believed what he experienced. We had intentionally programmed the wrong data into the simulation, for demonstration purposes, and our cleverness backfired. Simulation is an extremely powerful engineering tool, however, great care must be taken in its mechanization or the results may be totally misleading, and could even be catastrophic.

Following all this, on a beautiful spring day in the Mojave Desert (9 May 1969) John Manke made history by successfully flying the world's first supersonic lifting body flight. I don't think the actual flight was as exciting as the events leading up to it. From what we remember of the flight it was relatively uneventful except for going supersonic. Richard P. Hallion, in his book "On the Frontier" called this first supersonic flight "a major milestone in the entire lifting body program." Dick went on to say that "the HL-10 thus became the fastest and highest-flying piloted lifting body."

§

The first flight of the Douglas DC-10 Wide-body Airliner terminated at Edwards in 1970.

C-5A TESTS
by John W. Hicks

During the C-5A Cat.I/II performance test phase, the flight test crew headed for Kirtland AFB in Albuquerque, New Mexico in 1969 for high altitude takeoff and landing tests. As a young flight test engineer fresh out of college, I was assigned along with Al Rydman to man the weather vehicle (a GMC carryall), used to record runway weather conditions whenever we conducted such tests.

As the spear point group of the test team, Al and I, along with a couple of others, headed out in a C-130 with the weather vehicle to Kirtland. The journey went well enough, but I quickly learned how noisy a C-130 is in the cargo compartment. It was so loud and cold that I had to climb into the weather vehicle and close the door to get some peace and quiet, spending the rest of the flight there.

The Kirtland AFB Takeoff and Landing Tests
Arriving in Albuquerque, we quickly checked into a local motel and

Lockheed C-5A "Galaxy."

began making preparations for the C-5's arrival. I was, of course, very proud to be strutting around in our bright orange flight suits with the C-5 shoulder patch. Bright and looking like large pumpkins in our flight suits, we attracted a lot of attention around Albuquerque as harbingers of the "aluminum cloud" as the C-5 was known in those days.

Delay after delay kept the aircraft at Edwards and soon local TV stations were beginning to become skeptical that we'd ever show up for what would be a major local media event. Morning after morning we'd trudge into a nearby restaurant for breakfast in our bright orange pumpkin suits apologetically explaining that the C-5 was due any day. Finally, the aircraft approached the Kirtland runway at low altitude. Seen far out as it approached, it really impressed people how huge the aircraft was as it kept coming and kept coming, finally touching down to the gasps of all who saw her. Of course, we had to escort local dignitaries aboard to visit the aircraft, including for me the fun of showing stewardesses from local airlines around.

The test went fairly routinely, and we packed up to head back to Edwards after about a week. Westbound from Albuquerque, we asked the air traffic controllers where we could dump our usual huge ballast of 160,000 lbs. of water used to simulate cargo and control c.g. The air traffic controller suggested his alfalfa fields further west of town could use a good watering so he vectored us toward them. We had two huge 12-in. water dump ports on either side of the aircraft that could deluge an area quickly when we had to dump ballast. So over his fields we flew, not knowing whether the dumped water would actually wash away his fields or give them a nice thirsty drink. Away went the water in huge blasting streams over his alfalfa crop.

Not daring to look back, we pressed quickly on for Edwards, eager to get home. I'll always remember those C-5 days fondly; we were such a big, bruising aircraft for those days. As we headed west at 26,000 ft. into the setting sun, a commercial airliner passed us east bound. Upon receiving a report from air traffic control of the C-5 "aluminum cloud" heading at him, the airline pilot, in a monotone voice, coolly responded, "Roger, C-5 at 26,000, tail at 28!"

Those were the days!!

The First In-flight Engine Fire Experience

We were involved in the Cat I/II C-5A performance flight test program in 1970 conducting high altitude tests at around 40,000 ft. All the engineering test team operated directly onboard in conducting the flight, running the instrumentation recording station, etc. We all wore backpack parachutes and were trained for emergencies as a part of the flight crew, never suspecting we'd ever have to really use the training.

On the way back from Albuquerque on one such flight at around 43,000 ft. with Lockheed test pilot Carl Hughes at the controls, we had a hydraulic line break in engine number 3 on the left inboard wing. The hydraulic fluid immediately caught fire around the engine, engulfing most of the engine compartment. Unable to extinguish the fire, we had a major dilemma of whether to stay with the multi-million dollar aircraft or abandon it with at least the non-essential flight test team. The quandary of whether the fire would spread or cause an explosion during an attempt to return to base was quickly discussed among the crew. Certainly with the other three operating engines, it was felt a return to base could be done — but what to do with the flight test crew in the meantime?

The crew entry door had an escape slide that deployed just forward of that same number three engine for the crew to parachute away from the aircraft on. A large, perforated spoiler plate was suppose to deploy inflight between the engine and the crew door to keep the slip stream from sucking bodies into the engine area. Problem was, no one had ever had to try the system to that date and, looking out the small porthole window at the fire-belching engine, we didn't want to be the first to see if that spoiler concept would really work. Standing in the crew area with our backpack chutes already on, we decided we'd take our chances and ride it out with the air crew back to Edwards — praying all the way, of course!

So down we came, making a beeline for Edwards and Runway 04, all the time keeping a close eye on the flaming engine. As we landed on the main runway, the aircraft came quickly to a stop, and we flung open the crew door, looking for our ground crew rescue. Off in the distance heading toward us at high speed was a pickup truck and a fire engine. For what seemed like an eternity, we waited at the doorway until the pickup pulled up beneath the crew door and the burning engine. Carl sat at the pilot controls with full brakes on and kept the number three engine throttled up to keep air flowing through it in an attempt to retard the flames from spreading.

To our chagrin, instead of a crew ladder or gangway, the pickup had only brought a small trampoline device set in the bed. We were supposed to jump from the 20 ft. high crew compartment and hit that small trampoline in the truck bed. At that height the whole pickup looked no bigger than a postage stamp on the ground. I had thoughts of, "What if I miss that bed and hit the runway, severely injuring myself?", "Or maybe I'll just miss the trampoline and land between it and the edge of the bed?" With eager troops behind me ready to jump no matter what, I pulled my courage together and jumped for the postage stamp, landing squarely on the small trampoline. Quickly, we all sprang over the truck side, one after the other, and started sprinting madly down the runway away from the aircraft. Must have made record time, even with a parachute on!

After a sprint of 50 yards or so, the firetruck came whizzing by us headed straight for the burning engine. It had a large boom device with what looked like a large 18-in. shower head stuck out in front. Feeling safer now, we all turned after a few more yards just in time to see the fire engine charge full force right at the engine with its Don Quixote boom. A huge shower of fire retardant sprang from the shower, totally engulfing the engine and blew the fire ball right out the back end of the engine. With a sigh of relief, we all turned around and slowly started walking down the runway, thinking what a great day it was and how good terra firma felt under our feet.

MUROC DRY LAKE AND THE HEAVYWEIGHT
by M.J. Lehmann

In 1970, I was assigned as project officer/engineer to test the Collins Rotation/Go-Around Flight Director System to be installed in 700 plus KC/C-135 aircraft. Part of the contract required Collins to match the three and four engine take-off profiles depicted in the Performance Flight Manual. This required several heavyweight take-offs and since there were no other tests to be accomplished we would have to dump an enormous amount of fuel to reduce to the maximum landing weight of 200,000 pounds.

I obtained a waiver from OCAMA (Oklahoma City Air Material Area) to land the test bed aircraft at the maximum takeoff weight of 300,000 pounds using the dry lake bed since it would be impossible to stop on the 15000 foot regular concrete runway at Edwards at that weight.

We commenced heavy weight takeoffs on Thursday and after the first landing, everything seemed to be working perfectly: touchdown was glassy smooth (seven miles to get the flare just right), no brakes were needed because rolling resistance brought us to a stop right at the end of the main concrete runway, and all we had to do was taxi up on the main runway, fill up with water from the tanker truck standing by (the KC/C-135A's used 670 gallons of water for take-off thrust), and we were ready for another data point. There was one minor problem: the twin bogey main gear tires left 4 inch deep, four foot wide dusty ruts in the lake bed runway. However, the test pilots started at the left edge of the runway and just moved to the right a little for each subsequent landing. By the end of testing on Friday, we had destroyed most of the lake bed runway, but we needed only one more heavy weight landing and there was one small usable strip on the right edge of the runway. I thought things were going great.

On Monday morning, during his weekly tour of the facilities, the

Boeing KC-135.

base commander discovered the results of our previous week's testing. I received a phone call which essentially conveyed "You will NEVER, NEVER, EVER land that *#@!*+#! C-135 on the lake bed again!!! Is that understood???!!!

My calm reply was: YES SIR, YES SIR, YES SIR.

I believe Don Smith, Chief of Flight Test Engineering, and Jack Strier, my supervisor, received similar communications.

We continued testing off the main runway, and during our landing approaches I observed a small fleet of bulldozers, graders, sheepsfoot tampers, and rollers working on the lake bed runway. After two months though they could not accomplish what nature does in two weeks every spring: Rains cover the dry lake, wind and waves scour it smooth, and the sun bakes it brick hard.

The base commander got his revenge in a way. Since I was president of the Edwards Flying Club, he had my temporary fuel storage facility towed away. Ah, but that's another story.

SIMULATION
by Hank Klung

While at Edwards in 1970, I had an opportunity to "fly" a fixed-base (no seat motion) simulator that was designed to replicate the XC-142 and other VTOL machines. After about twenty minutes in the simulator, I had to quit because I felt nauseous.

At that time, I was taking a physiology course in a graduate program. The course required that I conduct an experiment and prepare a paper on its results. I decided to build my experiment around my experience with the simulator. I took eleven persons having flying experience ranging from none to about 4,000 hours, mostly in helicopters. I had each subject fly the simulator for about one-half hour, but I did not tell them that I was looking for their physical reaction to the experience.

The results were that the nausea was least in those subjects with no flying experience, and the most pronounced in those with the most helicopter experience. In fact, the pilot with close to 4,000 helicopter hours had to stop after about twenty minutes and vomited. My conclusion was that the simulator did not accurately simulate the dynamics of helicopters. There was a mismatch between what the pilot thought he was commanding and how the visual presentation indicated that the "aircraft" was responding.

The physiology instructor liked the paper. I gave a copy of it to the group responsible for the simulator, but I never learned what improvements, if any, were made to the device.

§

In 1971 the Air Force decided to terminate its Aerospace Research Pilot School and concentrate its efforts on the Test Pilot School. As a result the rocket-augmented NF-104 program was ended.

FB-111'S AND THE FINE ART OF "PIDDLE PACKS"
by John W. Hicks

As an impressionable young civilian flight test engineer, one of my favorite aircraft to fly was the FB-111A. As a performance engineer working with Clen Hendrickson and Gary Okubara in 1971, I was responsible for flying a large portion of the cruise performance missions. I flew the right seat, operating the data instrumentation system and keeping track of the flight card test points and conditions for the pilot. The pilot that shared this "adventure" with me is best left unnamed; you'll soon see why.

These range missions were often long, lasting hours and not the most exciting. Often times, as much as I loved to fly back then, I would have gladly given my seat up to the first "skywalker" that would have come along and paid me a dime. Those seat cushions seemed only an inch thick at best over a very hard metal surface. We were cruising along when the pilot could stand it no longer and had to relieve himself. He passed the control of the aircraft to me, and, as I tried to keep her "steady as she goes", he pulled out the French-made soft plastic "piddle packs" we all carried onboard. They were flat and shaped like a laboratory flask with a long, slender neck and a small, absorbent sponge in the bottom of the triangular-shaped container.

Wearing the khaki-green flight suit and a pair of gray leather flight gloves, he unzipped the lower end of the suit. Now I don't know how Frenchmen are built, but the neck on that thing was of an awfully small diameter — maybe the diameter of a quarter (or French franc?!) at best. Anyway, as the intrepid pilot began trying to insert his "private part" into the long, slender neck, I tried to keep my eyes forward and confine attention to flying the aircraft. Glancing sideways every now and then (just to see if he was making progress, you understand), I noticed he was having considerable trouble trying to "thread" the small opening, as it were. He was under a lot of "personal" pressure, needing to go badly, and was quickly losing his patience with the task (literally) "at hand." The whole curious event reminded me of a similar exercise of trying to stuff a marshmallow through a doorknob keyhole!

As luck would have it, he had progressed about 3/4-inch into the flask neck when air traffic control began asking us to "ident." By this time

General Dynamics' FB-111A.

the pilot was muttering darkly to himself — something about those darn blankedy-blank traffic controllers. Finally, not being able to progress any further down the flask neck, he couldn't hold it any longer and "let loose." The only problem was the entire "system" seemed to be under a lot of pressure (including the pilot's anxiety) and, sure enough, out popped the "device" in a wild gyrating whip like a fire hose at full throttle. With his not-so-graceful gray gloves on, he tried frantically to catch the errant thing as it merrily sprayed cockpit and canopy. Now cursing violently at himself and the radio (still blaring away at him), I tried to keep my cool and a straight face — with eyes forward.

When he finally caught "it" and shut off the flow, he reinserted the "monster" back in the flask, only to discover to his chagrin that he had so little left, he barely wet the sponge at the bottom. Alas, all was disaster in the cockpit as he finally acknowledged the radio call. It was curious to see — a very large wet spot on his flight suit from about the chest to the knees, soaked leather gloves, and that "ominous" telltale "golden" liquid trickling down the sides of both cockpit windows. Strangely, I was left unscathed throughout the whole ordeal. We, of course, had nothing left but to return to base and land.

The crew chief brought up the crew ladder on parking as usual, and the pilot, cool as a cucumber and without a word, was busy putting away his helmet and other gear. The sergeant looked with amazement at the cockpit area and the large wet spot on the pilot but spoke not a word. I'll never forget the looks and contorted grins from onlookers as we walked in silence across the ramp. Not a word was said, not a sound was made — he was the epitome of "cool." With straight jaw and steely eye, the pilot jaunted on as if nothing was amiss. That day really took on an extra special, double meaning for me in the description of test pilots as the "Golden Arm!!"

FLUTTER MAKES ME STUTTER
by M.J. Lehmann

In 1971 I was assigned as project officer/engineer to test the structural and flutter integrity of an RC-135U. One of the many modifications on this aircraft included a 250 pound antenna on top of the vertical stabilizer. Oklahoma City Air Material Area wanted to verify the maximum horizontal speed as depicted in the flight manual was still valid.

Mr. Haller, a General Dynamics structural engineer was assigned as a Tech Rep to supervise the instrumentation and telemetry installation. The rudder axis of the auto pilot was rigged as an excitation source of the vertical stabilizer. I wondered why we needed telemetry since there was plenty of room on board for instrumentation. In fact my little flight test engineer station in the middle of this empty fuselage was down right lonely. When they specified only a minimum crew (pilot, co-pilot, and me), and a chase plane to photograph the vertical stabilizer, I began to suspect this was a more serious test than I originally realized.

Test began smoothly with Mr. Haller and my supervisor, Jack Strier, monitoring the telemetry on the ground. After each run, they would analyze the read outs and pick what appeared to be the most critical frequency. I would set this in the excitation control panel, start the excitation for approximately 10 seconds while giving a count down on the radio so they could mark the time when excitation ceased. They would then measure how quickly the vibrations in the stabilizer damped out. We were inching up the speed in 5 kt increments for each data point. When we completed the data point for 405 knots, which is as fast as I had ever seen the aircraft flown, Jack advised to terminate the tests. I told him we had plenty of fuel for more runs, but he said "Nope. Bring it on down."

As I was reducing the data in preparation of writing the test report, I noticed the accelerometer trace from the tip of vertical stabilizer always reached a constant amplitude during excitation and then damped out as the excitation was shut off. That is until the 405 knots point; the amplitude continued to increase during the entire excitation phase. I took it into Jack and asked him what he thought would happen if we had gone up another 5 kts. He said "the tail might have come off". And I said "Th,Th,Th,Thanks Ja,Ja,Ja,Jack."

§

Apollo 17 was the final lunar landing of the Apollo program. It brought to conclusion a very successful, albeit expensive, space program.

A whole new generation of aircraft began to appear at Edwards. The Air Force conducted another flyoff for a new close support aircraft in 1972 between the Fairchild A-10 and the Northrop A-9. The A-10, affectionately known as the "Warthog", won the competition. A new air superiority fighter, the McDonnell F-15 "Eagle", made its maiden flight and began testing at Edwards.

BIRTH OF A NEW FLIGHT TEST TECHNOLOGY
by Lyle Schofield

The F-4 aircraft, while being a brute in terms of performance, has always been known as requiring a lot of skill to fly. The Tactical Weapons Delivery (TWeaD) I and II programs were initiated to make the F-4 handle more easily and be controlled more precisely. The TWeaD II program incorporated a very sophisticated three axis augmentation system which included control axis cross coupling and 14 gains or models with about 5 states each. As you can see, permutations and combinations for gains and models would tend to be overpowering. The prior approach for optimizing the control system was to use level flight open loop testing. I knew there had to be a way of optimization with the pilot in the loop, and so as Project Manager I suggested we use an air-to-air tracking procedure similar to that used by Tom Sisk of NASA-DFRC. This technique required using a pipper, fixed with respect to the airframe, to expose test aircraft motion by following the pipper motion with respect to the aim point on the target aircraft. The pipper motion was recorded on the gun camera film.

The first few flights using this procedure were failures because the pilot was closing the control loop using a low gain typical of the technique used in air-to-air combat where the pipper is "floated" onto the aim point. When we got together after the flight debriefing and became aware of the low pilot gain used, I instructed the flight test engineers to brief the pilot to consciously force the pipper back to the selected, precise aim point anytime it moved away from that point on the target aircraft. The objective was to have the test pilot functioning at as high of gain as reasonable. The results were spectacular, providing the pilot an immediate indication of the effects of control system gain changes. Subsequently the gains and models were completely optimized in seven flights over the whole flight envelope using constant g and windup turns. Interestingly, the gains arrived at with these techniques were slightly lower than those obtained with "standard" techniques, but were found to be fully applicable to all other flight tasks.

After looking at time history traces of pipper motion about the target aim point, but separated into pitch and yaw motions, it was apparent that the trace dynamics showed the kind of motion that should be easily analyzed by Fourier series methods. As Chief of the Flight Test Technology Branch, I had been involved with the development of flight flutter testing capability at AFFTC and was aware of our use of a Fast Fourier Transform computer routine for analyzing flutter dynamics. I recommended that we use the same technology to analyze the tracking data. Under the work and guidance of Tom Twisdale of AFFTC these techniques have evolved into the flight test and data analysis methodology known as System Identification From Tracking (SIFT). It has been possible using these methods to even extract aircraft stability derivatives and flight control system models; truly an advancement in the state of the flight test art.

FB-111A BOOMS
Sea Level Supersonic Accels in the FB-111A
by John W. Hicks

As a civilian performance flight test engineer, it was my responsibility to fly in the right seat of the FB-111A to obtain level acceleration performance. In 1972, my pilot and I were out over the Pacific Ocean just north of the Channel Islands off the Los Angeles coast conducting sea level "accels" at maximum afterburning power.

Westbound in a special military test corridor, we headed out to sea at full power only a hundred feet above the water. The intent was accelerate outbound, turn around, and re-accelerate back inbound to the east to obtain repeat data. The flight was impressive because, as I looked over the side, I could plainly see the bow shock wave hitting the ocean surface. The shock beat the ocean surface into a white foam that trailed out behind the aircraft as we skimmed along.

Suddenly before us, right in the middle of the corridor, was an unexpected merchant ship. We had understood shipping traffic was kept out of the area for military operations, but there they were unavoidably dead ahead. As we raked the ship at supersonic speed, we consoled ourselves that the entire vessel appeared deserted. It was ancient and completely brownish-orange from rust. Not a soul was to be seen on deck, so we assumed that maybe it was just an old, abandoned hulk used for targeting. We strained to catch anyone onboard and convinced ourselves as we headed on out to sea that no one could be onboard. We couldn't imagine what it would be like if someone were accidentally below decks when that shock wave boomed the ship's hull.

Turning around for the eastward run, once again we were supersonic with the bow shock savagely beating the ocean surface as we approached the ship. To our amazement, from out of the bowels of the ship, the decks were now literally covered with people shoulder-to-shoulder staring up at us as we approached. It looked like the "Princess Cruise" ship with strollers and shuffle board players on deck, but we were now right on top of them with no way to break off the flight path. So there we went — right over the top of them at full speed with a terrific bang!! I quickly looked back over my shoulder and strained to see the survivors. Don't know what I was really expecting — people jumping overboard, prone on the deck — don't really know. The pilot thought it was best if we didn't go back and check, so discretion being the better part of valor, we quickly pressed on east back to Edwards and landed. Never did hear if anything came of that unexpected experiment with sonic booms on ship hulls and "ship people."

Sonic Booms and Cal City Don't Go Together Well

In 1972, we were finishing up the FB-111A Cat. I/II performance phase with some maximum thrust supersonic acceleration tests in the Edwards High Altitude Supersonic Corridor. This test area extends above 30,000 feet over Edwards, running west-to-east from Gorman, California to Las Vegas, Nevada. As the "right seater" flight test engineer, running the data system and tracking the flight test cards, I always liked the "max accels" best because of the speed and the short flight duration.

Our 40,000 ft. max A/B accel began at Gorman and headed east to Las Vegas. Completing that run, we turned around and started a repeat point back toward Edwards. We noticed we were rapidly getting low on fuel, but, always wanting to "get that last data point in," we felt we could get the repeat point and still make Edwards for the landing. Streaking westward, we reached our aim speed condition just as the fuel low lights began to glimmer. Not wanting to flame out, we quickly retarded the engine throttles, performed a rapid pushover, and headed for the ground and the Edwards runway.

The only problem was that as we approached California City, a small desert community just north of the base, we noticed we were still supersonic and not decelerating quickly enough. Not having much other choice, we descended over Cal City, passing through 10,000 feet in a tight turn to make it back to the runway with the fuel low lights fully illuminated now. In a tight, supersonic turn that focused the aircraft shock right at "ground zero" in the middle of the town, we soon leveled out and made our approach to Runway 22 for a safe landing.

Hardly had we taxied back to the ramp when the Center Commander's phone began ringing off the hook from irate Cal City residents. Seems we managed to break some windows and crack some stucco walls in the process of trying to slow down over their fair town. The General knew just who the culprit was and rang us at the aircraft ops room just as we strolled in. Fortunately for me, just being a lowly junior flight test engineer, I didn't have to go to Headquarters with the pilot and explain what happened. Never did really hear the outcome or what the pilot's penance was.

HOW TO SPIN A GUPPY
by Richard E. Day

After Sputnik and during the space race to the moon, there was a need for hauling outsized cargo long distances in short periods of time. Some launch and spacecraft assemblies were of such dimensions that the geometrical confines of bridges, passes, and other restraints prevented their transport by rail. Out of these requirements grew the Guppy outsize cargo aircraft. First, the Mini-Guppy with an 18 foot diameter fuselage and eventually the 377 SGT (Super Guppy Transport) with a 25 foot internal diameter fuselage. Stepping into the cargo bay was like entering a domed stadium. It was constructed like the Hindenberg with stubby wings attached. However, the low fuselage fineness ratio made it look more like the aquatic guppy from which it got its name.

After the moon race, NASA kept the only Super Guppy and the Airbus Industrie Combine of Europe ordered two new Super Guppies from Aero Spacelines Inc. (ASI) of Santa Barbara, California to transport fuselages, wings and subassemblies of the wide bodied A-300 series of aircraft from the various European countries of manufacture to Toulouse, France for final assembly.

After the Guppies were built, they were required to complete FAA certification. (The U.S. FAA certification would comply with French requirements.) It was during the certification flight test program that the following, frightening incident occurred.

The flight test program had progressed to the heavyweight, aft c.g. stalls, the nastiest of the bunch. This series of stalls was made with the FAA pilot in the left seat. J.K. Campbell, the chief ASI pilot flew the right seat. I was seated at the flight test photo panel. During each stall approach and stall, I switched on the cine camera recording the instruments that were re-

Aero Spacelines "Super Guppy."

quired for data analysis. The stall approaches were made at various stall approach speeds. After two (perhaps three?) stalls, the last stall was made at a faster approach rate. At the moment of stall there was a loud "bang", a violent pitchup and roll to the left. We had actually entered into a left hand spin. The aircraft made three quarters of a turn while I was staring straight down at the Pacific Ocean wondering why I was there instead of behind a desk. After an eternity, a slow recovery and pullout was made. After achieving level flight I noticed that the airspeed instrument (on the photo panel) that was recording the airspeed calibration trailing "bomb" was reading 60 knots (the minimum) rather than the normal level flight value. I reeled in the "bomb" but it was not at the end of the tether tubing. It was gone.

After landing, an inspection revealed that there was a damaged section at the trailing edge of the right-hand elevator. This and other evidence indicated that during the violent stall and spin entry, the tether had wrapped around the right stabilizer and elevator and the stainless steel probe of the bomb had penetrated the base of the horizontal stabilizer and that the bomb had broken away and had fallen into the ocean. The probe was still embedded in the tail of the Guppy. Had the probe not broken off, the cable encircling the stabilizer/elevator may have frozen the elevator with predictable disaster.

It was mainly this incident that made the stall warning device (bright flashing lights and loud horn) a certification requirement.

The Vietnam war drew to a close in 1973.

NASA launched this country's first space station, the Skylab 2. It was manned the same year, and extended space research experiments were started.

The Automated Flight Test Data System (AFTDS), a real-time, CRT-based data display system, was inaugurated at AFFTC to support B-1 flight testing.

F-4 SIERRA EJECT?
by John W. Hicks

I don't remember the exact time frame or purpose of the flight test, but I recall it was about 1973 in a backseat F-4 flight over the Sierra Nevadas. We were flying southbound just west of Mount Whitney above one of the heaviest winters they had seen in a long time in the mountains. It was white as far as the eye could see with snow depths of 10 to 15 feet in most places. It looked awfully cold!!

I always seemed to have trouble getting used to a military aircraft's environmental system, especially fighters. Seemed like I used to get near frostbite below the knees and would be sweating profusely from the shoulders up. This made for an interesting thermal gradient problem when all this met right about the pit of my stomach with loads of morning donuts and hot coffee prior to a flight. For best comfort, I used to hate to fly in anything other than a summer-weight flight suit, no matter what time of the year it was.

So there we were west of Whitney well into the interior of the Sierra range and me without a winter flight suit or heavy jacket. I was feeling pretty comfortable and carrying on with our flight test work when the pilot saw both engine fire warning lights come on. Panic gripped me at first as we frantically looked around the cockpit for telltale signs of smoke or something. Not seeing anything immediately, we headed on southbound as the pilot began sending out "may day" calls. With double fire warning lights and no escort aircraft, we had no choice but to assume the worst, follow procedures and prepare to eject. We'd never make the desert or Edwards if there was a real fire somewhere on board.

The pilot called back to me to make preparations for bailout. For the uninitiated reader, the back seater always started the F-4 ejection sequence for both himself and the pilot. I dutifully put away my knee board and pencils, zipped up zippers, etc., and otherwise tidied up my cockpit area. I'd

McDonnell F-4 over the High Sierras.

never been in this situation before and, even though I had thorough survival training, wasn't quite sure what to expect. About this time it dawned on me that not only did I have only a summer-weight flight suit on with no jacket, but we had no food rations with our survival gear (who ever needed such a thing for flights on the desert?!) I quickly began to review the F-4 ejection procedures in my mind while the pilot was radioing our final position.

I remember looking over the siderail and seeing nothing but a wide expanse of deep snow. I could just see myself trying to hike out of the Sierras in heavy snow in the dead of winter with maybe a long wait for rescue. Deep snow and cold winter nights did not look inviting. Moaning to myself for my short sightedness, I located the ejection handle below the seat between my legs. Grasping it with both hands, I waited with dread while the pilot gave out his last "may days", intermittently asking me "Are you ready? Are you ready to pull?" Answering in the affirmative, I waited for his signal.

Just as I was about to pull with all my might on the handle, we heard a T-38 call from somewhere out over China Lake. He called out "Hey, if you guys can hold it a little longer, we can be there in five minutes and look you over." With great relief, we replied in the affirmative and held our course, waiting for the intercept. Sure enough, the T-38 soon came up alongside and looked us over top to bottom — no smoke, no fire, nothing! So with him as safety escort we gingerly turned eastbound and headed directly to Edwards.

Landing shortly afterwards, we soon discovered that we had a dual failure and false warning on the fire detection system — there was no fire or overheat!! We were, of course, relieved. But I thought back and shuddered on just how close I had come to having to "hit the silk" and try out all that survival training so deep in a Sierra winter and far from home. All that "excitement" on a civilian flight hazard pay that wouldn't have bought lunch on any given day!

X-24B VISUAL SIMULATION
by Bob Hoey

The X-24B Research Vehicle was a unique aircraft developed in the early 70s during the search for the "optimum" lifting re-entry shape. The configuration evolved from the AF Flight Dynamics Lab FDL-8 configuration which had a hypersonic lift-drag ratio of 2.5, about double that of the earlier lifting bodies. The FDL-8 shape was modified slightly so that it could be manufactured as a "gloved" structure around the existing X-24A Lifting Body. The development effort that followed occurred almost entirely within the Government, either AF or NASA. (Both contributed equally to the funding for the modification.) Martin manufactured the structural glove, but all simulation, control system design, subsystem modification, landing gear development and test, etc., occurred within the two government agencies.

The X-24B simulation used the time-shared computer equipment in the AFFTC Simulation Lab. There was a parallel activity in the lab which used a simulator cockpit under a point light source with a movable transparent light table. This system projected a horizon, runways and buildings onto a dome screen. The position of the light table relative to the light source was driven by the simulation equations to provide a visual simulation of attitude and altitude to the pilot. It was being used primarily for helicopter and VSTOL simulation work.

A few weeks before the planned first glide flight of the X-24B, some engineer got the bright idea that it would be very easy to transfer the X-24B simulation onto the light table system and we could practice visual landings with the X-24B simulation. (I'm afraid that engineer was ME!)

It only took a day or two to make the switch, and we were soon attempting to land the X-24B using only the visual reference to the horizon and runway. Results were quite puzzling. Occasionally the airplane could be landed easily, but on most of the approaches a divergent pilot-induced-oscillation (PIO) developed, followed by a crash. We had seen no evidence of PIO in our fixed-based simulation so these results were very alarming. John Manke, the NASA pilot who had been selected to make the first glide flight, had serious concerns about the validity of the visual simulation, but no one had been able to identify the problem. When word got to the Dryden NASA management (Paul Bikle) there was some talk of delaying the first flight until the "problem" could be resolved.

Manke was fuming! He spent several days trying to find the secret to landing the simulation, while constantly looking for discrepancies that would invalidate the whole effort. He finally identified the culprit. During one of the more violent PIO's he noticed that the bank angle on the 8-ball in the cockpit was not matching up with the horizon as projected on the screen. We found that it was very easy to rate-limit the light table. It would then lag behind and eventually get out of phase with the real attitudes as computed in the simulation and displayed on the 8-ball. It would rate limit at a relatively low roll rate, far less than could be generated by the little fighter-like X-24B. If no large roll rates occurred, the landing was easy — just like the fixed-base simulations. If the airplane roll rate momentarily exceeded the light table rate-limit, a PIO usually developed.

The first X-24B glide flight went off without a hitch. The handling qualities of the airplane were superb and compared favorably with those of a T-38. There was absolutely no tendency to PIO.

Once we mapped out the phase lag in the light table display system, we determined that the visual system was basically unusable. I believe it was discarded shortly thereafter. Helicopter simulations would have experienced some phase lag, probably enough to distract the pilot, but the simulated control response was usually not fast enough to allow a full-blown PIO to develop as it had on the X-24B.

§

President Nixon resigned in 1974.

Two more new aircraft flew for the first time at Edwards — the General Dynamics YF-16, a prototype light-weight fighter; and the North American-Rockwell B-1 bomber, a low altitude, high speed penetrator.

REPORT LEVITY
by Hank Klung

In 1974, I had the good fortune to be assigned as the chief of the Performance and Flying Qualities Flight Test Engineering Branch at the AFFTC. Ed Bradfield, one of the engineers in the branch, had prepared a technical report describing a technique which he had used to determine moments of inertia for an A-37B and a P-1127. The method involved balancing the aircraft on knife-edged beams and attaching springs to the aircraft extremities. Appropriate calculations could be made after determining the periods of oscillations after the aircraft was set in motion. Ed asked that a special cover be used for the report. Since it did not conform to the typical, sterile AFFTC format, I was hesitant to agree. But the more he talked, the more I became caught up in the humor of it. We put the cover on a limited distribution of the report. The cover showed a worried eagle spread-eagled across a knife edge and with its wings attached to springs. The report's title in bold Gothic lettering was "Great Moments of Inertia." I wonder how many copies are still around? I have mine.

F-111 ACCIDENT
by Clendon L. Hendrickson

Soon after I was assigned as project engineer to the FB-111A Program, I attended the usual Monday morning staff meeting conducted by the Test Force Commander, Col. Jack Gillette. I was introduced around the table and sitting next to me was a very amiable major named Jim Hurt. After status briefings by Maintenance, Operations, Instrumentation, and other department heads, the meeting was adjourned and the people went about their duties for the week.

At the next Monday morning staff meeting Major Hurt's seat was empty. He had gone to Test Operations on Sunday and after finding a navigator to fly with him had gone out to fly a gunnery mission. The F-111's had side-by-side seating and the ejection system was a capsule that separated from the fuselage with both crew members inside. After separation, an explosive charge was designed to blow a panel off the top of the capsule allowing a drogue chute to pull the main parachute out for descent. To ensure separation, this panel had four different modes of separation.

Evidently, during a gunnery pass the aircraft departed from controlled flight, and entered a spin. Since the F-111 had no spin recovery procedures, the crew ejected at about 16,000 feet. Even with all the redundancy built into the system, the top panel only partially separated allowing only the drogue chute to deploy and not the main chute. The crew members rode the capsule in from 16,000 feet. That was my introduction to the F-111 program.

FB-111A FLIGHT TEST PROGRAM
by Clendon L. Hendrickson

Although I was assigned as Project Engineer for the Performance and Flying Qualities of the FB-111A bomber, Steve Smith had the primary responsibility for the Flying Qualities and I for the Performance of the airplane. Major Bob Reidenauer was one of the project pilots. The FB-111A was a two-engine, variable-sweep wing, medium bomber capable of carrying both nuclear and conventional weapons and delivering them anywhere on earth at speeds up to Mach 2.2. It also had automatic terrain following capability at speeds up to 600 knots as low as 200 feet above the ground.

Early in the program we developed an anomaly with the T2 reset function of the engine. To help analyze the problem, an engine run was conducted after each flight with each engine at Military power then at Maximum Afterburner.

In preparation for a supersonic stability flight, Steve and Bob had flown out to a refueling area near Nellis AFB, Nevada to refuel. Some trouble was encountered and the fuel gauges indicated about 1200 to 1300 pounds of fuel before transfer started and a full bag of fuel was taken on board. Later, after a subsequent flight, Bob and I landed and taxied to the engine run-up area for the engine run. The gages indicated about 1400 pounds of fuel at the start of the run. The left engine was run up to Military Power for one minute, and then advanced to Maximum Afterburner, during which all the lights went out and both engines shut down. We had run out of fuel indicating about 1100 pounds on the gauges. Subsequent fuel tank calibrations showed that the gauges were out of Military Specification requirements and in the wrong direction. It also became obvious that it was possible to run out of fuel during a test program. I would say Steve and Bob were pretty lucky fellows.

FB-111A Flight Test Engineering team. L to r, front row: Steve Smith, Clen Hendrickson, John Hicks. Back row: Robert Draves, A1C Mike McLaughlin, Pat Henrich, Herman Shuping, unidentified.

During another flight, Bob and I had refueled across the Colorado River in preparation for a flight at 2.2 Mach at 50,000 feet to gather supersonic cruise data. After refueling we climbed to altitude, swept the wing back to 72 degrees and accelerated to 2.2 Mach. We had proceeded to a point about Soda Dry Lake when we experienced a compressor stall on number 2 engine. A compressor stall occurs when the airflow is disturbed and the engine regurgitates the air out the inlet. There was a tremendous bang and the aircraft yawed to the right and then the engine swallowed the air and we proceeded on. I had never experienced a compressor stall before and was amazed that the engine could produce such a loud noise without sustaining damage. Bob, always the cool one, had evidently experienced compressor stalls before, because all he said was, "compressor stall."

YF-17 PERFORMANCE TESTING
by Wayne Olson

In early 1974 I was assigned as the lead performance engineer on the YF-17 test program. The prototype YF-17 was to evolve into the Navy's F-18. Just a few months before the performance flying began I replaced Billy Boxwell as the lead performance engineer. Billy left for a job for the FAA in Seattle and ultimately became the chief of their regulations department. I had one captain (Paul Mathieuw) and two sergeants (Lee May and Benny Villamin) working for me. Paul took on the task of getting the new computer program called UFTAS (Uniform Flight Test Analysis System) working for us and in a parallel effort I coded up a program which I called SATFU (UFTAS spelled backwards) to reduce the data. In hindsight, perhaps we should have all directed our effort to getting UFTAS working for us but what if it wasn't working by the first performance flight? Also, the inflight thrust program was not yet available and as I recall it got to us too late to use for the performance analysis.

If I had bothered to learn UFTAS even a little bit I could have saved a lot of programming effort for SATFU. I could have used various UFTAS subroutines that would calculate air data parameters such as Mach number from airspeed and altitude and pressure ratio from altitude. I did a lot of reinventing the wheel. A positive fallout of that was I learned a lot about the mathematical relationships involved in air data calculations. My Fortran knowledge was limited also as I had not yet used the Fortran magic called a subroutine. But, I was not the only one with limited Fortran knowledge as we had a new program then called DPS (Digital Performance Simulation) and it didn't use subroutines either. I sure did learn a lot about performance by figuring out how DPS computed missions with climb, cruise, turn, accel, and descent segments. Six years later I wrote a new version of DPS which

Northrop YF-17 (precursor to F-18).

did the same computations as the old DPS but with much improved Fortran. Most of the programming was done by David Nesst and the end result was a very much easier to understand and use program.

Since I didn't know how to read data from an engineering units tape I decided to ask the contractor to provide me with print outs of basic engineering parameters such as airspeed, altitude, total temperature and fuel flow. We (myself and the two enlisted troops) then keypunched 13 parameters onto 2 computer cards per data point for each performance flight. The typical maneuver consisted of about 30 data points. I think we had something like 20 maneuvers per flight and about 15 flights which we flew in two weeks so my advanced math computes we punched about 18,000 computer cards in a two week time period. Boy, did we have a good time on that. Of course if I was knowledgeable on reading computer tapes we could have avoided all of that and on future work that I did I always had someone working with me that knew how to do that stuff and I never did learn how to use UFTAS but did become quite expert on the computations that UFTAS performed and relied on other computer specialists to handle the mechanics of making UFTAS work.

As you all know the YF-17 lost the competition with the YF-16 but became a winner when the Navy decided to buy the F-18.

SOMETIMES WE WIN!!!
by Fred Stoliker

In the days of piston engines, it was common to prepare a plot of power required versus speed (Piw - Viw) with all data corrected to a weight (Wiw). The concept was similar to making plots of lift coefficient versus drag coefficient (without Mach effects) — and the underlying principle was that all data should fall on a single line. Then, after fairing "best fit" curve to the Piw - Viw data, we would then correct that curve back to the standard weight for a particular weight and altitude condition. Then, supposedly, all of the data would be consistent. Great concept! However, we noticed that for some cargo aircraft the "standard" curve would not always match too well with some data for given weight and altitude conditions. The differences were usually small and since we couldn't find any problems with the instrumentation, we concluded that the differences were just one of those anomalies that occurred.

As the speed and weight capabilities were increased primarily with the advent of turbo-props (C-130s and C-133s), these departures from the best fit "iw" curve got considerably bigger and couldn't be ignored. While we were all debating the probable causes of this anomaly, Bill Magruder (who, by the way, was an outstanding test engineer before moving on to become an outstanding test pilot and ultimately, a Presidential Science Advisor) noted that most of the planes to which this occurred were "tail-loaders" — YC-122, C-123, C-130, C-133. After this "revelation, we collectively looked at the reports of these aircraft to see if there were other characteristics in common. Lo and behold, the guys in Performance Engineering and Flight Research Branches found that all of these aircraft had missed their cruise drag estimates by between 10 and 35 percent, the deviations from the standard "iw" fairings were at the lightest weights and the lowest speeds, they all had a nose-up pitching tendency at high sideslip angles, and none of them had any stall warning with the flaps and gear down! After a good deal of brainstorming, we concluded that the relatively sharp "break" in the lower fuselage contour to accommodate the "tail-loading" capability was the major culprit for the differences from the "iw" curves (the lightest weights would result in a lower angle of attack at a given airspeed and this, in turn, would result in the largest difference between the airflow along the bottom of the fuselage and the slope of the fuselage ramp area).

This seemed to be pretty much a nice little exercise in observation and deduction until the SOR (Specific Operating Requirement) was issued for a jet-powered cargo-carrying aircraft with cargo-loading and unloading capabilities that almost dictated a tail-loading capability. Several of us put our heads together and felt that we should notify the SPO that this configuration could result in the characteristics noted above. A letter was drafted and sent to the SPO alerting them of the back-ground of this type of configuration and the types of problems that could be expected. The letter also urged that the SPO consider incorporating in-flight refueling capability to extend the range when carrying maximum cargo. After about a six-month delay and a number of phone calls inquiring as to the status of the letter, we were informed that the SPO and their advisors in the Labs had considered the potential problem and had the situation well in hand. Lockheed was selected as the winner and built the C-141. (We had made copies of our letter available to all of the competing contractors).

Guess what? The C-141A missed its cruise drag estimate by 10 percent, had a nose-up pitching tendency at high sideslip angles, had no stall warning in any configuration, and had no aerial refueling capability.

When the SOR that resulted in the C-5A was circulated for comment, I went back to the SPO for a test planning conference and discovered that the SPO Chief of Flight Test was a former Wright Field flight tester. While having a beer, I told him of the problems we had encountered with previous tail-loaders and he asked for further info. We gathered up copies of the previous information and letter and sent it to him. (And I can't remember if the SOR had a requirement for aerial refueling). At about that time Lockheed issued a model of there proposed entry and it looked very much like a scaled-up C-141 — blunt gear pods, a sharp break of the lower fuselage to accommodate the tail-loading capability, and the upper fuselage had a rather abrupt "bump" to accommodate the wing carry through structure. After his review, he called to say that he found our data very interesting and was having some detailed discussions with the aerodynamicists at the competing contractors.

When the C-5A was built, the gear pods, the nose gear door, and the wing carry through area had been smoothly faired (and it had aerial refueling). When the tests were complete, the cruise drag was 5 percent lower than estimated.

P.S. When we saw the first 737 at Edwards, we were all struck by the very sharp break in the fuselage behind the pressure bulkhead. I asked the Boeing rep if they had missed their drag estimates and reminded him of the material that I had given him on the tail loaders. He said no sweat — everything was under control. About four months later he came back and asked if I still had copies of the material — said that they had an interest in the problems noted (and several of engineers commented to me about the large vortex generators place around the lower fuselage near the "break.") I can't swear that our data affected the later 737 mods but the "break" is much less pronounced on the 737-200 and 737-300 than on the early 737s.

P.P.S In 1990, I (Bob Hoey) assisted in a flight test program on the C-141 specifically designed to obtain data to update the AF crew training simulators. We found that we could not match the steady sideslips with the derivatives and equations normally used in simulations. In order to match the elevator deflections we had to add a new term — Cmbeta — pitching moment due to sideslip.

§

Twenty eight years of highly profitable research using air-launched, rocket powered aircraft, came to an end with the final powered flight of the X-24B, piloted by NASA's Bill Dana.

Another flyoff program got underway for a new light weight fighter. General Dynamics' YF-16 won the competition, but the losing YF-17 later emerged as the Navy's F-18.

The F/FB-111 testing had dramatically pointed up the need for an avionics test and integration facility at the test site and efforts begin to design and implement this concept.

X-24B CONCRETE RUNWAY LANDING
by Johnny Armstrong

The X-24B was the last in a line of lifting body research aircraft that were tested by a joint NASA DFRC and USAF AFFTC flight test team between 1963 and 1975. Preceding it was the plywood M2-F1 that was towed aloft by a C-47 Goonie Bird, and the metal lifting bodies that were air-launched rocket-powered; M2-F2, M2-F3, HL-10, and the X-24A. The potato shaped X-24A was modified by Martin Marietta Corp. into the pointed-flatbottom X-24B. The arrow shape was optimized to provide high max L/D at hypersonic speeds thereby providing higher maneuvering crossrange and glide capability during reentry. The purpose of the tests were to evaluate, indeed to develop, the low speed (below Mach 2) characteristics of this class of vehicle as applied to future spacecraft returning from orbit with more class than splashing down in the ocean.

The X-24B was powered by the 4-chamber XLR-11 rocket engine burning LOX and water alcohol. Earlier versions had powered the X-1 during Chuck Yeager's first supersonic flight. At the beginning of the lifting body program a group lead by NASA manager John McTigue collected the needed rocket engines from various museums. The X-24B was launched from the one of the X-15 B-52B motherships from 45,000 feet. The propellant was usually exhausted after about 135-140 seconds and the X-24B was then a high-speed glider. The X-24B attained a maximum Mach number of 1.752 and a max altitude of 74,100 feet during the 26 month flight program.

I was fortunate to have been the AFFTC flight planner for the earlier X-24A and part of the X-24B flights until I became the AFFTC project manager after Bob Hoey moved into the job of preparing for the Space Shuttle program. Dave Richardson of AFFTC took over the helm of flight planner.

The flight planner was the guy, next to the pilot, that knew the most about the flight. He gathered the data requirements from the researchers, created the initial flight plan on the man-in-the-loop simulator, trained the pilot using the simulator, served in the control room guiding the mothership to the launch point, advised the flight director, analyzed the flight data and help publish the flight report. This was a great job.

Now it was 5 August 1975 as John Manke the NASA project pilot, in a spaceman looking pressure suit, climbed into X-24B S/N 551 under the right wing of the B-52 mothership S/N 008 (Balls 8). It was about 45 minutes from take off and the LOX boiloff from the X-24 was floating hazily around the mating area. This would be the 27th flight of the X-24B and it was scheduled to end with the first landing of an unpowered low L/D aircraft in the narrow confines of a concrete runway. All other flights of this type of low L/D aircraft had landed on the forgiving expanse of Rogers Dry Lakebed. The X-24B was the first lifting body to have what was considered a usable nosewheel steering system that was necessary to perform a safe landing on a concrete runway. In addition, the aircraft had excellent handling qualities during landing. Why were we doing this? Because it had not been done before and the Space Shuttle, which was in final construction was some day going to have to land on a regular runway after initial flight tests to the lakebed.

During the early planning for the flight we presented a briefing of our plans to the AFFTC commander and his staff. We were fortunate in that the AFFTC commander at the time was Major General Bob Rushworth, the pilot who had flown the hypersonic X-15 more times than any other pilot; 34 flights. He understood what we were doing and why, but he changed our plans. We had picked the planned touchdown spot 2500 feet from the approach end of the runway 04. This meant we would have another 12,500 feet of runway, plus miles of lakebed runway after that if needed. Rushworth felt that we should plan to touchdown 5000 feet down the runway. As he put it "I will forgive you if you land long and end up rolling onto the lakebed, but landing short of the concrete runway will be unacceptable." We implemented his direction and John Manke set about flying many simulated landings in the F-104 reestablishing his ground check points for the landing pattern. There was a white line about six feet wide at the 5000 foot point that was used by the Test Pilot School. So the target was defined and the challenge had been made. Shucks! He had to change his final approach aim point from a road to a lone Joshua tree on the desert floor.

Manke is now a passenger in the cockpit of the X-24B under the wing of the B-52 as it takes off runway 04 for the 50 minute climb to 45,000 feet and the launch point near Cuddeback dry lake 60 miles north of Edwards. He is reviewing the flight in his mind, in particular the practice he had early that morning in the F-104 to get a feel of how to compensate for upper altitude winds during the landing approach. Approaching the 17-minute point, chase pilot Bill Dana made a tension-relieving radio call.

Bill: "Hey John, did I tell you my cousin that tends bar in Oildale had invented a new drink?"

John: "No, what was it Bill?"

Bill: "It's milk of magnesia and Vodka and he calls it a Phillips screwdriver."

Then right back to business. The NASA 1 Flight Director, Lt. Col. Mike Love breaks in: "OK, we're at 17 minutes, go fuel tank vent and give me some more left yaw trim." From then on to launch things got busy setting up and verifying the X-24B was ready for launch.

"3 - 2 - 1 - Launch.....OK, John, it looks like a 3 chamber profile." One of the 4 chambers of the XLR-11 rocket engine failed to light after launch. So a preplanned alternate profile was flown. Data maneuvers were still accomplished as this was a normal data collecting flight to continue the definition of the aerodynamics of the X-24B. The planned flight was to have achieved a maximum Mach number of 1.5 and max altitude of 70,000 feet. The alternate 3-chamber flight achieved 1.19 Mach and 57,000 feet. The engine burn time was 153 seconds and the total flight time was 7 minutes. The safety feature built into this flight plan was a commit point 3 miles from the normal turn point for a 165-degree turn from 24,000 feet to final approach for the Edwards main runway 04. If, before this commit point, any one of the critical systems needed for a safe runway landing was not performing satisfactorily, then a turn could be made to a landing on Rogers lakebed runway 36. As the X-24 approached the commit point Mike Love radioed, "And you're about 1000 high, you can plan on landing on 04, we have good systems down here." From here down Manke would later describe his work load as extremely high, as well as his own gain. He would relate the work load to a Cooper-Harper rating of 7. John performed the flare and tracked the target white line perpendicular to the runway as the aircraft decelerated and descended. The left wheel touched down just ahead of the white line and the right wheel touched down just beyond the white line. John had split his goal right down the middle. Even as the X-24B was rolling to a stop, the ground crew next to the runway confirmed his accuracy, to which Love radioed from the control room, "Yea, it looks to me like you got that line for about a $1.00's worth up here." (Obviously a friendly before-flight bet.)

Two weeks later Lt. Col. Mike Love repeated the event by flying flight 28 to the same runway. Bill Dana, another NASA lifting body pilot and former X-15 pilot, flew two powered flights to the lakebed. His second

X-24B lands at the "spot" on Edwards' main runway.

flight was going to be the last powered flight in the X-24B and we all sensed that this was going to be the last flight of a rocket powered air launched research vehicle for a while, so we gathered around the aircraft on the lakebed for and "End of an Era" photograph. Now 20 years later there still has not been another rocket research aircraft although there were two close attempts; the National Hypersonic Flight Research Facility/X-24C effort and the more recent National AeroSpace Plane/X-30.

The last effort in the program was to get an evaluation of the X-24B flying qualities by non-lifting body pilots and to provide the chosen individuals experience that would be valuable in the upcoming Shuttle Program. The pilots were selected to fly two glide flights each. The two NASA pilots were Einar Enevoldson and Tom McMurtry. The Air Force pilot who later became a Shuttle Commander was...Major Dick Scobee.

§

It's fitting to end this volume of Edwards flight test stories with the X-24B as the next era in the Edwards test saga picks up with the Approach and Landing tests of the Space Shuttle in 1976 and the eventual flight into orbit. Also, many new aircraft began showing up at Edwards; F-15, F-16, B-1, etc. But that's another volume...

To sum up the feeling that we the authors experienced while participating in the events described in this book we will steal the opening statement by John Manke at the post flight debriefing for the above flight. It presents the feeling of singularity of purpose that was always part of a flight test program. IT has been called many things over the years. IT is the team....Test Team, Combined Test Force, Joint Test Force, et al; but it was always a team and its job was to test.

"OK, this was flight B-27-40 on 5 August and it was a beauty. First off, that is my last scheduled flight in the airplane, and I have mixed emotions about that. I was really looking forward to today's flight, because this has been one of the biggest challenges I have had so far in the program and it has been one heck of a big thrill; just practicing and working with it. And I guess even a bigger thrill than that is working with the fantastic bunch of people that it takes to put this on. Any of you at the crew briefing yesterday are aware of the many people that were involved in something like this. That's more of a thrill I think than any thing else around here, just watching everybody working and watching them put all the pieces together. I couldn't pick any one person or any 10 or 20 out that contributed, but to all of you I say, "Thank you very much; it was really great; without each and every one of you we couldn't have done something like this today. All the folks did a lot of nice things today."

...........DATA OFF"

*Edwards photographer Gene Furnish standing by a photo chase T-38.
"Th-thee, aa, th-thee, aa, th-that's all folks!"*

EPILOGUE

To the knowledgeable reader it will be obvious that we have only scratched the surface of the actions that were taking place at Edwards. For example, where are the stories about the F-102, F-104, F-106, A-7, A-10, B-70, C-141, Navy programs, commercial programs, "black" programs, etc.? Maybe our modest efforts on this book will convince people to take pen in hand (or more likely, notebook computer in lap) and provide these — or any other — missing stories. Perhaps a new collection of stories is in order relating the later years at Edwards.

If you were a flight test engineer or test pilot associated with activities at Edwards AFB, and are interested in adding to the Edwards heritage, contact us at:

Flight Test Historical Foundation
44916 N. 10th Street West
Lancaster, CA 93534
661-723-1574

or check our website at; http://www.avbot.org/fthf

ADDENDUM

Col. Townsend's response to Al Phillips XB-52 story on pg. 61;

"This story causes me to do something I should have done a long time ago, and that is to publicly apologize to you, Al, for my "words" on said flight. I knew that you were not going to die at that altitude, but that is no excuse for my actions. I would rather remember your performance on a Phase IV test where we were trying to go to 60,000 feet and you lost your ability to transmit on interphone. You kept a steady stream of notes on the trolley you had rigged up saying "go for it."

Guy Townsend"

To order additional copies of this book contact:
AFFTC Museum Gift Shop
P.O. Box 57
Edwards, CA 93523
(661) 277-8050

A GLOSSARY OF TERMS, ACRONYMS AND ABBREVIATIONS

AAF	Army Air Forces/Army Air Field
AB	Afterburner
accelerated stall	A stall test conducted at load factors greater than one
accels	Tests where the aircraft is accelerated at a given altitude at constant power (usually to measure excess thrust or static longitudinal stability)
AF	Air Force
AFB	Air Force Base
AFFTC	Air Force Flight Test Center, Edwards AFB, California
AFSC	Air Force Systems Command
Angle of Attack	(AOA or alpha) The angle between the fuselage centerline and the relative wind, measured in the plane of symmetry of the airplane
Angle of Sideslip	(beta) The angle between the plane of symmetry and the relative wind, measured in the plane of the wings
anhedral	Negative dihedral (wing tips lower than wing root)
ASAP	As Soon As Possible
ASD	Aeronautical Systems Division (located at Wright-Patterson AFB, Ohio — site of Aeronautical SPOs and WSPOs)
APU	Auxiliary Power Unit - A small unit used to provide aircraft utility power (electrical,hydraulic, compressed air, etc.) before the main engine is started or after engine shut-down
ARDC	Air Research and Development Command (Predecessor to the Air Force Systems Command - AFSC - and the current Material Command - MC)
ARI	Aileron-rudder interconnect - a device to apply rudder deflection proportional to the commanded aileron deflection
autorotational landing	A landing made by a helicopter/rotary wing aircraft after a power failure utilizing the residual momentum in the rotor blades to reduce the sink rate at touchdown
Base Ops	Base Operations — The terminal facility for transient and other non-test aircraft flight operations
BLC	Boundary Layer Control — A general term describing any method to smooth the air flow over a wing in order to increase lift and/or reduce drag
BOQ	Bachelor Officer Quarters
CAA	Civil Aeronautics Administration (forerunner of the FAA)
CAP	Civil Air Patrol
Category Tests	The series of tests on a new aircraft that leads from first flight to operational use in the fleet (replaced Phase testing about 1958) I - Contractor Development Test II - AF Development Test and Evaluation; conducted by AFFTC and 4950th Test Wing III - Operational Test and Evaluation; conducted by the Using Command
CBR	California Bearing Ratio — A measure of surface hardness in which a rating of 100 is equivalent to the load bearing capability of crushed limestone
cg/c.g./CG	Center of gravity
Check Climb	Climb tests flown to check the time required, fuel used, distance covered, etc., to reach a given altitude utilizing the speed for best rate of climb as determined from other kinds of tests (accels, sawtooth climbs)
cinetheodolite	A photographic device that continuously records an object's time-space-

	position information
closed loop	A mode of control in which the controls are deflected continuously based on visual or measured observations of the aircraft motions
Cnb/Cn beta	Yawing moment coefficient due to sideslip; the measure of an airplane's static directional stability
CP	Power Coefficient
CO2	Carbon Dioxide
compressor stall	A reaction to a disturbance in the airflow to a jet engine in which the compressor blades stall (usually quite suddenly and violently)
Constant W over delta	Aircraft weight divided by the atmospheric pressure ratio. A flight test parameter that permits an aircraft to be flown at the same angle of attack, even though weight is changing due to fuel being burned
C sub L	(CL) Lift Coefficient - A non-dimensionalized parameter for determining the lift produced by an airplane
CT	Thrust Coefficient
CT&M	Cargo, Trainer, and Miscellaneous Section (a part of the Flight Test Operations Division at AFFTC - sometimes called Cargo Ops/Cargo Miscellaneous Operations/etc.)
Dead Man's Curve	This curve defines the combinations of height and velocity that must be maintained by a helicopter in order to safely perform an autorotational landing after a sudden engine failure (also called the height-velocity curve)
degrees of freedom	(DOF)In simulation, the number of simultaneous acceleration equations being solved in real time by the simulator computer. (6 DOF includes 3 translational and 3 rotational equations that completely describe the motions of a rigid body.)
Delta Wing	A triangular wing shape. Named after the Greek capital letter delta of the same shape
deep stall	A mode of post-stalled flight where the airplane achieves a trimmed, stable condition with the wing and tail at very high angles of attack (60 to 90 degrees) and control surfaces are completely ineffective
DFRC	(NASA) Dryden Flight Research Center
dihedral	The angle of the wing relative to the horizontal plane of the aircraft. (For positive dihedral the wing tips are higher than the wing root.)
dip sticks	Calibrated sticks that were marked to show the fluid level of a vessel when the sticks were dipped in the fluid
DPS	Digital Performance Simulation
Duct Splitter	A device placed in the duct of an F-104 to prevent resonant, alternating flow between the left and right inlets
Dutch roll	An oscillatory rolling and yawing motion resulting from coupling between the yaw and roll axes of an aircraft. (The name was derived from the similarity to the smooth, side-to-side motions of a Dutch ice skater.)
dynamic stability	A measure of the frequency and damping characteristics of oscillatory motions of an aircraft
DYNA SOAR	(DYNAmic SOARing) Name acronym applied to the X-20 program
EAI	Electronic Analyzers, Inc. A manufacturer of computer equipment
EAFB	Edwards AFB
Eddy/Eddie	shorthand reference to Edwards AFB
EKG	electro-cardiogram (a measure of heart functions)
engine chop	Rapid movement of the engine power control device to the idle power position to simulate an engine failure
engine-out control speed	The minimum speed at which a multi-engine aircraft can be controlled after the sudden loss of power on one or more engines
FAA	Federal Aviation Administration

fixed base	A simulator in which the pilot's seat does not move
FRG	Federal Republic of Germany
FTE	Flight Test Engineer
flying bedstead	A flying simulator that contained a propulsion system and projected control system (so named because of a resemblance to a four-poster bed)
G/g	Force of gravity
GEDA	Goodyear Electronic Data Analyzer - an early analog computer
GD	General Dynamics
Golden Arm	A term applied to flight test pilots
Herrington Manual	An engineering manual compiled during the early 1950s that contained approved test techniques and data reduction procedures (Authors were Russell M. Herrington and Paul Shoemacher)
HSFS	(NACA) High Speed Flight Station - predecessor to the NASA Dryden Flight Research Center
ICBM	Intercontinental Ballistic Missile
JP-4	Jet engine fuel (basically kerosene)
IBM	International Business Machines
instrument corrected data	Data that has been corrected for the errors that exist in the instrument used for a measurement
intercom	Intercommunication (aircraft internal communication system)
Iyy	The aircraft's moment of inertia about the wing axis
KIAS	Knots indicated airspeed (the speed shown on a pilot's instrument)
knot(s)	Speed measurement in nautical miles per hour
LA	Los Angeles
L/D	Lift/drag ratio - the ratio of an aircraft's lift to its drag - a measure of the gliding capability
load factor	The ratio of the normal acceleration experienced by an aircraft divided by the acceleration of gravity (G/g)
LOX	Liquid Oxygen
LTV	Ling Temco Vought - an aircraft manufacturer
Mach Number	The ratio of the speed of an aircraft to the speed of sound
MC	Material Command
MCAS	Marine Corps Air Station
MASH	Mobile Army Surgical Hospital
MC	(Air Force) Material Command
MDs	Medical Doctors
M&M Hangar	Maintenance and Modification Hangar (where test aircraft were maintained and/or modified)
Mil Spec/MIL SPEC	Military Specification
moving base	A simulator in which the pilot seat moves in response to pilot or other inputs to the simulation
MPE	Military Preliminary Evaluation (a short AF evaluation during contractor Category I testing)
NAA	National Aeronautics Association (or) North American Aviation
NACA	National Advisory Committee for Aeronautics (Predecessor organization to NASA)
NAFEC	(FAA) National Aeronautical Flight and Engineering Center
NAS	Naval Air Station
NASA	National Aeronautics and Space Administration
Navajo Trail	A runway on the South Rogers lakebed; named for the Navajo guided missile which was tested there
Non-rated personnel	Personnel who have not received formal training as an aircraft crew member (pilot,navigator, weapons officer, etc.)
Normal Rated Power	The maximum power that can be extracted continuously from an engine
OCAMA	Oklahoma City Air Material Area

OJT	On-the-job training
oscillograph	A device that photographically records various items on the aircraft that have been fitted with instrumentation sensors
open loop	A control mode where the aircraft is disturbed but controls are not deflected to react to the disturbance
Pacer	An aircraft with a carefully calibrated airspeed system. The pacer would fly alongside a test aircraft to calibrate the airspeed system on the test aircraft
P&W	Pratt and Whitney - aircraft engine manufacturers
Performance landings	Landings performed to determine the minimum distance from a 50-ft. height to a complete stop for the optimum setting of flaps/slats, etc.
Performance takeoffs	Takeoffs performed to determine the minimum distance from brake release to clear a 50-foot obstacle using optimum flap/slat/etc. Settings usually at maximum power (5-minute rating) or maximum AB power
Phase Testing	Types of testing conducted prior to about 1958: I - Contractor Development II - Air Force Performance and Stability III - Contractor Development (if aircraft passed Phase II) IV - AF Performance and Stability V - All-weather Tests VI - Accelerated Service Tests VII - Employment Suitability VIII - Unit Operational Employment Testing
Photobox/photopanel	An Instrumentation Panel that was lighted so that photographs could be taken of the instruments and provide a photographic record of flight conditions
Photo Theodolite	Pictures taken through a grid to record time-distance-height measurements
PIO	Pilot Induced Oscillation - A serious control problem resulting from a mismatch between the pilot's ability to command control deflections and the aircraft's capability to respond to those deflections
pipper	A dot in the gunsight which predicts where bullets will impact
Pitchup	An abrupt increase in angle of attack brought about by an instability in the pitch axis (Usually associated with T-tail configurations)
Pitot-static system	A system for measuring the airspeed-altitude of an aircraft (pitot measures the total/dynamic pressure of the airstream, static measures the (near) ambient/undisturbed pressure of the airstream)
pulses	A sharp input to the pilot's control used to excite movement about an axis
Rated Personnel	Those who have completed a training program that qualifies them as a member of the normal complement of an aircraft (pilots, co-pilots, weapon system operators, etc.)
Rudder lock	A condition that results when the rudder pedal control force gradient reverses and the rudder "floats" to full deflection
RMI	Reaction Motors, Inc. (builders of the XLR-11 rocket engine)
RPM/rpm	Revolutions per minute. Here, an indication of the power output of a jet engine.
Rotary Wing Section	A Section of the Performance Engineering Branch whose personnel were charged with the engineering aspects of determining an aircraft's performance and flying qualities
RTB	Return to Base
RTO	Refused Takeoff
SAC	(USAF) Strategic Air Command
SAS	Stability Augmentation System
Sawtooth Climbs	A series of climbs conducted to determine the speed for best rate of climb

	(Named for the "sawtooth" appearance of the trace of time vs. altitude)
Service Ceiling	The altitude a which an aircraft has a rate of climb of 100 feet per minute utilizing maximum continuous power
SFO	Simulated Flame Out - a condition where flaps, speed brake, engine power setting, landing gear, etc., are set to approximate the thrust-drag relation ship that would exist if the engine were inoperative (windmilling)
simulator	A computer, programmed with the equations of motion and the aerodynamic coefficients of a particular aircraft, tied to a cockpit which allows a pilot to simulate flight in that aircraft
Speed/Dive Brakes	Aerodynamic devices that increase aircraft drag and cause a decrease in speed
Speed Power Tests	Tests flown to determine the power required to fly at a set speed for given weight and altitude
Spiral stability	The tendency for an aircraft to return to a selected bank angle when disturbed from that bank angle
SPO	System Program/Project Office - An organization responsible for managing the acquisition of a new aircraft
stall	The loss of control about any aircraft axis as the airspeed is reduced, usually caused by separation of the air flow over the top of the wing
static stability	A measure of an aircraft's inherent tendency to return to a trimmed flight condition after a disturbance
Static Pressure	The pressure that would exist in undisturbed air at a given altitude
STOL	Short Takeoff and Landing
TAC	(USAF) Tactical Air Command
TDY	Temporary Duty
Technical Observers	Official AF designation of Non-rated civilian and military personnel authorized to fly on test aircraft
Test Ops	(Flight) Test Operations (Division) - the organization at Edwards to which the test pilots were assigned
theta	Aircraft pitch attitude - the angle between the horizon and the aircraft longitudinal axis
TPS	(USAF) Test Pilot School at Edwards AFB
Trailing Bomb	A small (10-12 inches long), bomb-shaped device that was towed behind an aircraft to measure "static/ambient" atmospheric pressure
T-tail	An aircraft tail configuration where the horizontal tail sits on top of the vertical fin
UFTAS	Uniform Flight Test Analysis System
US	United States
USA	United States Army
USAAF	United States Army Air Forces/US Army Air Field
USAF	United States Air Force
Ventral Fin	A fin extending from the bottom of the fuselage to enhance directional stability
VIP	Very Important Person
VOQ	Visiting Officer Quarters
VOR	VHF (Very High Frequency) Omnidirectional Radio Range
VSTOL	Vertical/Short Takeoff and Landing
VTOL	Vertical Takeoff and Landing
Water injection	The use of water injected into a jet-engine to lower tailpipe temperature and increase engine mass flow thereby increasing thrust
Weight and Balance Hangar	A large hangar at AFFTC containing scales and other equipment to determine the weight and balance (cg location) of aircraft
wind-up turn	A test maneuver where aircraft load factor is continuously increased (usually until stall is experienced or aircraft limits are reached)
Wing rock	An inherent lateral oscillation that precedes the stall on many modern

	fighters
Wright-Patterson	Wright-Patterson AFB
WSPO	Weapon System Project Office - successor to the SPO
WWII	World War II (1939-1945)
YAPS head	Yaw-angle, Attack-angle, Pitot-Static head. A special test device mounted on a nose or wing boom to provide measurement of angles of sideslip and attack plus pitot and static pressures in relatively undisturbed air
8 ball	The 3-axis attitude indicator on the pilot's instrument panel

Aircraft Descriptors

C	Cargo
F	Fighter
B	Bomber
A	Attack
FB	Fighter-Bomber

Prefixes

A "J" before any of these designator shows the aircraft has received permanent modification.
A "K" indicates a tanker capability.
An "N" indicates a temporary modification.
A "Y" indicates a prototype of an intended production model.
An "X" indicates an experimental model that may become a production model. For example, NKC-135 - the "N" stands for a temporary modification to a production aircraft, "K" indicates the aircraft is a tanker, "C" shows the aircraft was procured basically to carry cargo.

FRED STOLIKER served at the Air Force Flight Test Center from 1950 to 1981 where he served in various engineering and management positions. He retired from the AFFTC in 1981 after serving seven years as the Center Technical Director. He retired from the Camarillo Center of Computer Sciences Corporation in 1991 after having served as that Center's Technical Director. He edited an "Introduction to Flight Test Engineering" for NATO's Advisory Group for Aerospace Research and Development which was published in 1995. He has a Bachelor of Science degree from the University of Michigan, completed the Stanford-Sloan Executive Management Program, and holds an MBA from Golden Gate University.

BOB HOEY worked at the Air Force Flight Test Center for 32 years beginning in 1955. During that time he was involved in the flight testing of most of the Century Series fighters (F-100 to F-106) and many of the joint AF/NASA research airplane programs such as the X-15, the lifting bodies, the X-29 and the Space Shuttle. He supervised the flight testing of the first Air Force fly-by-wire airplanes (F-4, SFCS, A-7 DIGITAC and YF-16). He has recently worked as a consultant, primarily in the analysis of flight test data for flight training simulators. He holds a bachelor of science degree from the University of Washington, and a masters degree from the University of Southern California.

JOHNNY ARMSTRONG is currently an engineering manager at the Air Force Flight Test Center. He has been involved in flight test of aircraft and rockets for 39 years (38 of which have been at Edwards AFB. He participated in the flight test of the Redstone Missile, Saturn I, SA-16B, YB-58A, F-104, X-15, the lifting bodies (M2-F2, HL-10, X-24A, X-24B) and the Space Shuttle, and is currently leading the Air Force Flight Test Center's test engineering team preparing for X-33 and X-34 tests. He received his bachelor of science degree in Aeronautical Engineering from the University of Alabama.